Introduction

'All in Good Faith' contains thirty-six simplified stories, designed to be read aloud during primary school assemblies. The book contains six stories from each of the following major world faiths: Buddhism; Christianity; Hinduism; Islam; Judaism; Sikhism. Each section begins with a short introduction giving an outline of the main beliefs of that faith. A large page format has been used for easy access. The simple line drawings may be used with an O.H.P. if desired.

Topical Resources publishes a range of Educational Materials for use in Primary Schools and Pre-School Nurseries and Playgroups.

For the latest catalogue:
Tel: 01772 863158
Fax: 01772 866153
e.mail: sales@topical-resources.co.uk
Visit our Website at:
www.topical-resources.co.uk

Copyright © 2004 Ann Preston
Illustrated by Caroline Hesford
Printed in Great Britain for:
Topical Resources,
Publishers of Educational Materials,
P.O. Box 329,
Broughton, Preston PR3 5LT by:
T. Snape & Company Ltd.,
Boltons Court, Preston.

First Published May 2004
ISBN 1 872977 82 0

Contents

C000138074

Disclaimer

'All in Good Faith' is not an academic study of major world religions to be picked over word-by-word but a collection of stories and traditions assembled to help young children take a glimpse into the diverse and rich world of many faiths and beliefs. Every effort has been made to check the authenticity of each introduction and the choice of stories used. Where various spellings of the same name have been encountered, the publisher has endeavoured to use the one that appears to be the most common. For help with these matters the publishers are indebted to various members of the 'Preston Faith Forum' and other followers of the faiths dealt with in the book especially:

K. H. Kumur

Jill Simone Barlass

Moulana Farook Kazi

Rev. David Braunold

Rev. Peter Sheasby

Christine Sheasby

S. Wear

The book has been written and published 'in good faith'. If any major errors have unwittingly been made in the production of this work the author and publisher sincerely apologise and will be pleased to make corrections where necessary.

# Buddhism

INTRODUCTION

- Buddhism began 2,500 years ago, in Asia. There are now Buddhists in most countries throughout the world.

- Buddhism is a religious practice, which expresses its philosophy through daily life.

- Buddha means 'The Awakened One'. Buddha travelled around telling others about his discovery of Nirvana, the enlightenment, wisdom and sense of peace which rises above pain and suffering.

- Buddhists try to follow the 'Eight Steps of the Eightfold Path'. These are not rules, but ideas of how people should behave towards one another. One of these steps is meditation or contemplation, which can be used to learn about the deep, inner self.

- Buddhists believe that nothing is permanent and that the world and everyone in it constantly changes.

- They believe that everything in the universe is connected, that every word, thought or deed will eventually have a result.

- Buddhists try to feel compassion for all creatures and believe that they should never cause anyone or anything to suffer. This is one of the five precepts, or promises, which Buddhists follow.

- The precepts are:

  1 Not harming living things, but helping others.
  2 Not taking anything which you are not given, but being generous.
  3 Not being greedy, but being content.
  4 Not telling lies or speaking unkindly, but telling the truth.
  5 Not drinking alcohol or taking drugs, but keeping a clear mind.

- Being a good friend is vital to Buddhists.

This story tells of the birth of the Buddha. Buddhists celebrate the life of the Buddha in a special festival called Wesak. On this special day, Buddhists decorate their homes with flowers and lamps and everyone is especially kind and generous to others.

THE BIRTH OF THE BUDDHA

Long, long ago, King Suddodana and his wife, Queen Maya, ruled a small kingdom in the north of India. They lived in a magnificent palace in the kingdom's glorious capital city, Kapilavastu. The palace walls were encrusted with jewels and the gardens bloomed all year round. The King was known to be wise and honest and Queen Maya was not only as beautiful as a perfect lotus blossom, but was also kind and good.

One night while she was sleeping on her perfumed couch in the palace, Queen Maya had a dream. She dreamt that she saw a dazzling light shining down from the sky and out of the light came a pure, white elephant with six tusks and with a lotus blossom in its trunk.

When Maya woke up she was filled with a great feeling of joy, which she could not explain. She dressed in her brightest colours and went for a walk in the palace gardens. There she sat on a shady bench and sent her maid to ask the King to come and talk to her. She told him of her dream and requested that he send for interpreters so that it could be explained.

The interpreters said that the dream was very good news and that soon the King and Queen would have a very special baby son, who would grow up to be rich in vision and who would become great and good and be praised by all. The King and Queen were overjoyed and felt they must give thanks and celebrate their good fortune. The King called for his servants and told them to take money from the palace treasury and give it to the poor. He told them to take food to the hungry and drink to the thirsty and give all women flowers and perfume.

Months went by until Queen Maya knew that it was time for her son to be born. She went to the King to tell him that she would go to her father's home in the next kingdom, which was the custom at that time. On the way there, she stopped to rest in the beautiful garden of Lumbini, which was filled with flowers and fruit trees, birds and bees. It was a clear night in May and the moon shone brightly. It was there that Maya gave birth to her son.

Then a rumbling earthquake shook the earth and the world was flooded with light. Throughout the land there was a great feeling of peace and joyfulness as people forgot their worries. Everyone seemed to feel that this was no ordinary baby.

There was a great rejoicing in Kapilavastu when Queen Maya returned. They named the baby Siddhartha, which means 'The one who brings about good'.

One day, shortly after Siddhartha was born, an old man called Asita visited the palace. He had travelled for many days, on foot, to see the baby. Asita was widely respected and known to be a wise and holy man and a great teacher. The Queen brought the baby to him and he looked at Siddhartha for a very long time and then tears began to roll down Asita's cheeks. "Whatever is it?" asked Queen Maya, "Is something the matter with our baby? Can you, with your great wisdom see something wrong with him? Please tell us, for we love him so much."

"Don't be afraid," said Asita gently. "Siddhartha will grow up to be a wonderful man, a very great man. Look at the light shining from his fingers, a sign of the fate which awaits him. He will have a great many choices. He could become a mighty ruler or the greatest and most famous king the world has ever known or he might choose to become a great and wise teacher. I am crying not because there is anything wrong, but because I am already a very old man and am sad that I may not have the chance to learn all that he will teach us. I am crying with the wonder and happiness of it all."

Asita then turned and left the palace, rejoicing that he had been fortunate enough to see a baby who was very special, a baby who would grow up to be wise and good and would show people how to live in harmony, love and peace.

In her dream, the queen saw an elephant with a lotus blossom in its trunk. The lotus flower is very special to Buddhists. The lotus plant grows in muddy water, but the flowers rise to the surface to blossom. This can be seen as similar to human beings, who, though full of faults and failings, can grow to be better people. By being kind and loving to others, we will grow and blossom.

This is another story about Buddha. It tells how Buddha showed his gratitude to a woman who gave all she had, to help others.

(In Asia, it is customary for people to show the extent of their gratitude by the way they receive gifts, rather than by what they say. Their gratitude is greater when they stand or take with two hands, than when they remain seated, or receive with one hand.)

GIFTS FOR THE POOR

One day, Buddha was collecting gifts to take to the poor. People came to him to show how kind and generous they were and how much they cared about people less fortunate than themselves.

The King came to Buddha. "I shall give that house you see over there, Lord Buddha. I shall also give all that land which you see around it."

Then the Prince arrived. "Lord Buddha," said the Prince." I have brought many fine jewels which you may give to the poor."

Then came the Lords. "Lord Buddha," they said," we have brought gold and silver, which you may distribute to the poor people."

They were followed by many rich merchants, who brought bags of money.

As these people came with their gifts, Buddha smiled at them, but did not stand up. He took their gifts and held out his right hand to thank them.

Just then, a very old woman came to Buddha. She was thin and bent over and was dressed in old, torn clothes. She held out a small orange to Buddha. "Here you are," she said. "I know it isn't much, but it's all I have. I was just going to eat it when I heard you were collecting for the poor."

Immediately, Buddha stood up and went to her. He held out both hands to receive the orange and to thank her.

The King, the Prince, the Lords and the merchants looked on in amazement. They did not understand why Buddha had made such a fuss of the old woman. They went to him and the King said, "Lord Buddha, we brought you really expensive and fine gifts, yet you held out only one hand and did not get up. This old woman brought you only a little gift yet you stood and received it with both hands. Why was that?"

Buddha looked at the rich men standing before him. "You are all wealthy men," he said, "who gave only a little of what you have. This old woman is poor and has given everything she has. Her love for others is greater than yours, so I thanked her more than I thanked you."

This story tells of a young man who was not satisfied with his share. His greed caused him and his family to lose what could have been their good fortune.

THE ENCHANTED LAKE

Tashi lived at the foot of a high mountain in Tibet. Everyone said that there was an enchanted lake at the top of the mountain and that the lake was filled with treasure. Tashi dreamed of climbing the mountain, seeing the beautiful lake and about the wonderful things he could buy with the treasure. He planned to climb the mountain.

His parents warned him against it. They told him about the dangers people spoke of and of the difficulty of the journey, but most of all, they spoke of the fearsome spirit who guarded the lake and who would not let anyone near it. They told him of the great many people who had wanted to reach the treasure and had tried and failed.

Tashi would not listen to their warnings, however, so early one morning, wearing warm clothes and carrying an empty sack in which to put the treasure, he set off. It was a long, hard journey. Higher and higher he climbed until the slopes were icy and dangerous. The wind howled and the mist swirled around him. He was alone and afraid. He pulled his coat tightly around him as, battling against the wind, he scrambled over yet another pile of rocks and there he saw it. The lake gleamed before him.

There were many lakes in Tibet, but never had Tashi seen one like this. It shimmered as if it was made of pure gold. He just knew that the lake was full of treasure and he ran towards the shore. As he stood by the water's edge, a figure emerged. It was a huge woman wearing a brown cloak and a heavy golden necklace. She had long, wild, black hair from which the water streamed. Her face was terrifying.

When he saw her, Tashi wished he had heeded his family's warnings and he trembled before her evil stare. Then he remembered how long and hard his journey had been and he became bolder. "I have come for the treasure in the lake." he said. "What do you have for me?" "I have more for those who need, than for those who demand it," the wild spirit woman answered. The boy stood his ground and said, "Well, I want my share." She scowled at him before saying, "Then take it and go." With that, the figure vanished into the water.

Tashi put his hand into the cold, sparkling water and felt something. He grabbed at it. "I've got the treasure," he shouted as he looked at the three gleaming gold coins in his hand. He looked back at the water and was about to turn and go when a thought came to him. "If I can find three coins so easily," he said to himself, "there must be many more in this water. Why should I settle for just three? If I go and get help, we can take lots more." He dropped his sack and tossed the three large coins back into the lake, before hurrying down the mountain back to his home.

When he got there he told his father about the journey, the lake and the woman. "The spirit woman is no danger to us," he said, "we can take two bags and fill them up with gold. We will be rich."

Tashi convinced his father that his plan would work, so back up the icy slopes went Tashi, with his father following him. The journey was long and hard, but at last they reached the lake, which was just as Tashi had first seen it, shimmering like gold. As they neared the shore the large, spirit woman rose once again from the water. "Now what do you want?" she asked. "I gave you three golden coins when you demanded your share. Was that not enough for you?" Tashi spoke up, "My father wanted to see the lake for himself. Give him a share too and we won't bother you again."

A sudden mist swirled round the spirit and she scowled at them both before vanishing again into the water. The boy and his father reached into the water grabbing at whatever they could. Each managed to grab hold of three large golden coins.

"It seems that we can only have three each," said the father. "Yes," said the boy, his eyes now gleaming with greed, "but the lake is clearly full of money. If we bring the rest of the family and a yak to carry the load, think how rich we will be then. We will never have to work again."

They threw their bags down and tossed the six coins back into the lake before hurrying down the mountain to tell all their relatives the plan. By the time they reached home and told their story, it was too dark to climb the mountain again that day, so they decided to rest before getting ready.

They were so sure that they had defeated the spirit of the lake and they were so excited about their future wealth that they thought they should celebrate. They opened the storerooms where the food for the next year was kept, opened bottles of wine and beer and boasted so much to their neighbours about how rich they were going to be that soon the whole village was celebrating with them.

The villagers ate and drank well into the night and before going to bed, the family looked at their empty stores. "Never mind," Tashi said, when he was told that all their supplies had gone. "Soon, we shall be so rich that the store rooms can be filled to the brim with much finer stock. We shall be able to buy whatever we want."

The next day, Tashi led his parents, his brothers and sisters, his aunties, uncles and cousins up the mountain. With them plodded a yak carrying huge, empty bags. The nearer they got to the top, the more Tashi boasted about his find and how clever and brave he had been to venture up the mountain. He reminded them that they had not wanted him to go, yet soon they would all share great wealth because of him. Everyone became very excited and talked about all the things they would buy on their return.

"We're nearly there," shouted Tashi. "It's just beyond those rocks." They hurried forward to climb the rocks to see the wonderful sight Tashi had told them about and there, sure enough, was the lake. This, however, was not the lake which Tashi had described to them. The water was not golden, but dark and murky. They stood and waited, but no spirit woman appeared. There was only the fog and the mist and the silence.

Tashi hurried nearer to the shore. "Here I am," he called loudly. "I have come back for more coins." Nothing happened. He put his hand into the icy water and grabbed for coins. There was nothing but mud. The others all tried. All day long, they waded in the icy, muddy water but the only things they found were pebbles. They set off to make the long journey home, exhausted, cold and hungry and bitterly regretting that they had used up the contents of their storerooms.

Tashi and his family had learned a very hard lesson. But for their greed, they would still have had the golden coins which had been their share and the food to last for the rest of the year.

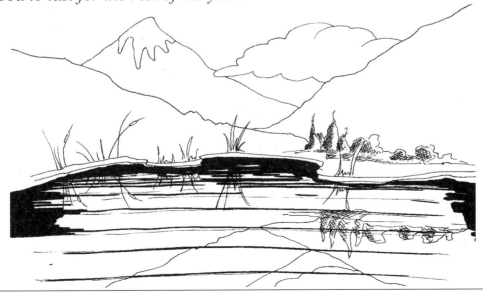

Buddhists believe that there is great happiness to be found in helping others. This story tells how the Buddha helped a woman to find her own happiness.

THE MUSTARD SEED

One day the Buddha was walking along the road when he came to a river. It was a very hot day and he was dusty from the road, so he stopped and bent down to splash some of the cool water on his face.

When he had finished washing, he looked up to see an old woman. She knelt down beside him to drink from the river. Her clothes were old and torn, her face was tired and her arms were thin and dirty.

"Oh," she wailed, "I am suffering so much. Can you help me?" The Buddha looked at the old woman kindly. "What is the matter?" he asked. "What do you want me to do for you?" "Just look at me," she moaned, as she pointed at herself with her long, bony fingers. "Just look at my clothes. Look at the sores on my arms. I am tired, hungry and ill."

She went on to tell the Buddha how she had once been wealthy and had owned her own house and some land, but that now she had nothing but a bowl of rice to eat. She pleaded and pleaded with the Buddha to help her, to heal her and to get her riches back. The Buddha answered that everyone has some suffering in life, that she had described life as it is.

The old woman became very angry and then started to cry. "I will not listen to you," she said. "I was not born to suffer like this and yet you refuse to help me." The Buddha, seeing that she did not understand what he was trying to say, reluctantly told her that he would help, but that she must do exactly as he said.

"Yes," she agreed, "anything, anything, I will do anything to get my riches back." The Buddha asked the old woman to bring him a mustard seed. She stared at him in astonishment. "What," she asked, "a mustard seed? Is that all that I should bring, only a mustard seed?"

The Buddha replied, "Yes, but the seed must come from a house where the people have never had any troubles, suffered anything or been sad. Find this seed and I will use it to banish all your suffering and sadness."

"Oh, thank you, master, thank you!" she said. The old woman hurried away to find a house which had known no suffering, so that she could get the mustard seed which was to bring her happiness. The Buddha continued his journey.

Many weeks later, the Buddha came back along the same road, to the same bit of river. There, he saw the old woman again. She was kneeling by the river, washing clothes and spreading them on the rocks to dry in the sunshine. He heard her singing happily as she washed. She turned, saw him and smiled.

"Hello," said the Buddha, "have you found a mustard seed yet?"

"No," said the woman "I did look, but every house I visited had sorrow and troubles, far worse than mine and there have been so many people who have needed my help."

"Are you still looking for the mustard seed then?" asked the Buddha. "I suppose so, when I have time," said the old woman. "There is still much to do. These clothes belong to a poor family with a very sick child, and they need them to be washed quickly, so I must get on." She smiled at him and went on scrubbing the clothes and singing to herself.

The Buddha, too, smiled. "You no longer need the mustard seed," he said, "You have discovered for yourself the joy and riches of helping others."

The Buddha went on his way.

This story tells of a young boy who cared a great deal about his grandfather and tried to make others see what might be the outcome if they continued with their selfish plans.

THE OLD MAN AND THE DOKA

There was once a very poor family who lived in a small, broken down house in a part of the country where the land was not fertile so it was difficult to grow food. The man worked hard to provide for his wife and their young son. Also living with them was the man's father, who was now too old and frail to help with the work.

The woman complained all the time about having to care for the old man. "We have no room for him," she grumbled. "We can only just manage to feed ourselves and we shouldn't have to worry about feeding him."The old man, therefore, was neglected and given only scraps to eat. He had to sleep on a small mat on the floor in a dark corner of the room. There were no blankets and his thin body shivered and shook with the cold.

The boy, however, loved his grandfather very much. Whenever the father was working out in the fields and the mother was busy outside, the boy and his grandfather would sit together and play games with pebbles and sticks. The grandfather would tell the boy tales from his youth, from when he was strong, could work, and times were better. Every chance he had, the boy saved some of his food and, when his parents were not looking, he gave it to his grandfather.

One day, they were sharing some bread when the mother came in and caught them. She did not say anything just then, but later that night, when the boy and the old man were asleep, she grumbled and grumbled about it to her husband. He listened to her complaints, but said that there was little they could do.

Time went on and still the work was hard and food was scarce, but the boy managed to save some to share with his grandfather. Each night the wife would complain to her husband about having to care for the old man and one night, the boy woke up to hear his parents whispering. They seemed to be talking about his grandfather. He lay very still and listened.

"Think how much easier it would be with just the three of us. Do you think it would work?" he heard his mother ask. " I don't see why not," said his father. "We'll talk about this more tomorrow, when we've had more time to think."

The next night, the boy pretended to be asleep and again listened to his parents talking about how they could rid themselves of the burden of caring for the grandfather. "If we take him and leave him somewhere along the road, how can we make sure he doesn't find his way back to us?" asked the wife. "We must take him so far that he can't walk back," said the husband. "But he's frail and he can't walk very far, I'd have to carry him." The man thought about this a bit longer and began to feel sorry for his father. "I don't like to think of him out there on his own, though," said the man. "Oh, don't go changing your mind," said the selfish woman. "He'll probably find some people who'll take pity on him and take him in. He'll be okay." The woman started to grumble again about the extra work and so the husband gave in and they went on hatching their plan.

The boy was horrified that they could consider such a thing, but he said nothing and the next night he listened again. They had now decided to put the old man in a "doka", which is a cone shaped basket, used in India and Nepal, to carry heavy loads. The basket is held in place by a piece of fabric which goes around the forehead of the person carrying the load. The man was to go to market the very next day to buy a doka.

When his father returned with the basket, the boy confronted his parents. "I have heard you plotting," he said. "How can you think of doing such a thing to my grandfather?" "Why?" said his mother. "We are only using the doka to carry him to a place where there are people who care for the elderly and the sick. He will have a much better life there than he can have with us."

The boy was not convinced that this was true, but did not see what he could do to stop them. They placed the old man in the basket and the wife helped to fasten it onto her husband's back.

As the man started to go off down the track, the boy shouted after him. "Father," he called, "don't forget, when you've got rid of my grandfather, to bring the doka back home." "What for?" asked the man. "We have no use for a doka! There is no need to keep it."

"Oh yes there is," said the boy. "I'll need it for you in a few years time, when you get too old and sick to help with the work and you need feeding."

The man listened to his son's words. He stopped and turned around. Very slowly, he came back to the little house, where he placed the doka on the ground and very carefully, he lifted his father out. "I'm sorry," he said.

The man turned to the boy. "Thank you, my son, for reminding me what is important."

From that day forth, though times were still hard, and food was still scarce, they shared what little they had.

Buddhists believe that true peace and happiness are not brought about by worldly possessions, but by the goodness which comes from within. This story tells how a magical golden elephant helps a boy realise what his path in life will be.

THE GOLDEN ELEPHANT

Long, long ago in India, there lived a boy, whose name was Gopala, who had a golden elephant. The moment that Gopala was born, the baby elephant just appeared in the family's garden, as if from nowhere. Everything about the elephant was golden and he was not only very beautiful, but was also a kind and gentle animal. Gopala and his elephant grew up together like brothers. Wherever Gopala went, the elephant followed and crowds would gather to see them.

One day, a messenger from the king, came to Gopala's home. He told Gopala's family that they must take the elephant to the palace. "All golden elephants belong to the royal household," he said. "They cannot be kept as pets by ordinary, common people."

Gopala was very upset. "My elephant is like my twin brother," he said. "How can the king just take him away from me?" Gopala's father tried to comfort him. "Do not worry, the king is jealous and greedy, but maybe justice will prevail. However, we must go to the palace as the king commands."

Gopala stroked his elephant's gleaming trunk. He was so afraid that his dearest friend would be taken from him, but he whispered, "Don't worry, all will be well." The elephant knelt so that Gopala and his father could climb onto his back for the journey to the palace. When they arrived, the king dismissed them with a wave of his hand. "Be on your way," he said, "and leave the elephant with me." The king had a great many gold rings on his fingers and they gleamed in the sunlight, but not one of them shone as brightly as the elephant's golden back. The king looked at the elephant greedily, proud that he was now the owner of such a beautiful and precious animal.

Gopala looked at his father in dismay. Surely his father would do something. Surely his father would not let the king keep his dear friend, but Gopala's father just bowed to the king and turned away. "Come," he said to Gopala, "we must return home."

As they began their journey, Gopala pleaded with his father, " You MUST be able to do something," he said, "the king has stolen my elephant. It is wrong and unfair." His father carried on walking. "Be patient, my son," he said.

As they approached the edge of the forest, Gopala heard a familiar sound. He couldn't believe it, for there in front of him stood his golden elephant, waiting for him. "Is this why you told me to be patient?" Gopala asked. "How did you know he would be here?" His father smiled and said, "Last night, I had a dream that all would be well and that your elephant would be returned to you."

They returned home happily and never heard from the king again. Gopala, however, thought about what had happened. He felt sad that he lived in a land where a king would steal from his subjects because he was greedy and they had something he wanted for himself. As he grew older, Gopala became aware of many things which were unjust. He noticed that some people were greedy, like the King, and were jealous, and never satisfied with their lot.

More time passed and Gopala gradually turned away from worldly, material things. He began to reflect more, thinking and meditating. He gave away almost all his possessions, and helped the poor. Finally, he decided he wanted to get away from ordinary life. He wanted to go to the Buddha and become a monk.

Gopala climbed onto his elephant's back and set off to find the Buddha, who welcomed him. "Come now," he said, "into a simple and pure life." So, Gopala became a monk, wearing a monk's yellow robes and bearing a begging bowl in his hands. From then on, he, like every other monk, would own nothing and would beg for rice each day. He had a new name, he was known as Kanakavatska.

Everything about his old life, except the golden elephant, was left behind. Kanakavatska learned to stop thinking about possessions. He no longer yearned for anything as he was free from all those concerns, but the elephant stayed by his side as he went about the countryside caring for others and teaching.

Kanakavatska was a good monk, but he attracted a great deal of attention as he went about teaching, because people were fascinated by the golden elephant. Some of them talked only of the elephant and did not listen to his words. When the Buddha heard of this, he sent for Kanakavatska. "Your elephant is creating a disturbance," he said. " You are not to blame, you are a good monk, but your pet must go."

Kanakavatska was sad, but was ready to release his friend. "He has been like a brother to me for so long," he said, "and I want him to feel the same peace and contentment that I do."

"We are all brothers," said the Buddha, "and we all long for peace. Your golden elephant was sent to you to lead you to the right path and because you were a good person. He must now be released to help someone else."

Kanakavatska went to the elephant, who was quietly chewing leaves at the edge of the forest. "Dear one," he said, " thank you for your friendship, but now, we no longer need each other. I am free and content and I want the same for you. Go in peace."

Three times, Kanakavatska said this and the third time he said 'Go in peace' his elephant disappeared before his eyes. For an instant a spot of shimmering gold hung in the air and then it was gone and there was silence amongst the trees.

Kanakavatska had found that by giving up worrying about material possessions, leading a good and simple life and concentrating on helping others, he could find real peace and happiness.

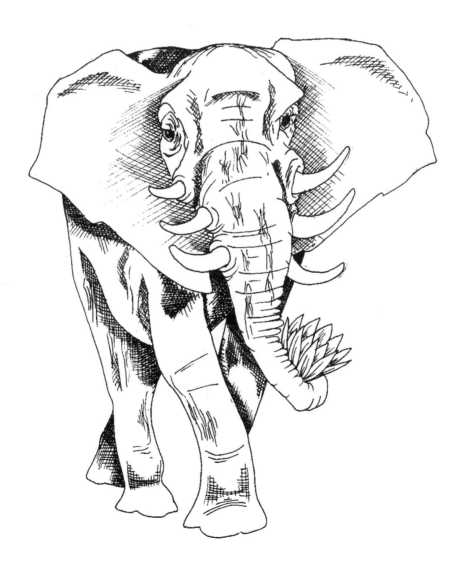

✝ Christianity

INTRODUCTION

- Christianity began about two thousand years ago and is now practised by many people throughout the world.

- Christians believe in one God who created the universe and gave people rules to live their lives by, as written down in the Holy Bible.

- Christians believe that the Son of God was born as a human being named Jesus Christ (which means Saviour).

- Jesus was a wise teacher and healer who travelled the land telling people about God. He taught that God loves everyone and that people should love God and love one another.

- At the age of thirty-three Jesus was put to death on a cross by powerful men who were afraid of his influence. Christians believe that by his death Jesus offered people God's forgiveness for their sins. They also believe that three days after his execution God raised Jesus from the dead.

- Christians believe Jesus gave his followers the Holy Spirit to help and guide them.

- Christians meet together in churches on Sundays to praise God, to pray, and to learn about Jesus.

Jesus told this story to help people understand that it is what you do, rather than who you are or where you live, which makes you a good friend or neighbour.

THE GOOD NEIGHBOUR (THE GOOD SAMARITAN)

Jesus was a teacher, so people were always asking him questions. One day a lawyer came to Jesus and asked, "What should I do to make sure I get into heaven?" Jesus answered, "What does the law say?" The man answered, "You should love the Lord with all your heart; and with all your soul, and with all your strength, and with all your mind; and your neighbour as yourself."

"That's right," Jesus said. "If you do all of that, you will be able to get to heaven." But the lawyer, thinking he could ask Jesus a question that could not be answered, asked, "But who is my neighbour?"

Jesus answered him by telling this story:

One day, a man was travelling from a far away city, when suddenly he was set upon by a gang of thieves. The thieves took everything he had, and then they beat him up and left him by the side of the road.

As he lay there in pain and misery, he heard footsteps. "Ah! Someone is coming!" he thought. "I hope it isn't one of the same men who beat me, coming back to find out if I am dead." He waited and listened for what seemed like hours, sure that if it was not the thieves, it would be someone who would help him. No one came to him, however, and when he looked, he saw a man and heard his footsteps fade into the distance.

It had been a priest who had come near, but when he saw the man lying beside the road, he decided to take a different track, because he was in a hurry and did not want to be bothered.

After a little while, he heard footsteps again. This time, surely someone would come to his aid.   He wanted to call out and get the attention of the person walking by, but he was in so much pain, all he could do was moan. "Surely this person will see me and help?" he thought anxiously.

This time the man who passed by was a Levite, a well-known teacher in the temple. Surely he would want to help. But when the Levite saw the man lying by the side of the road, he looked down, turned his head and walked right by, completely ignoring the poor man.

Before long the man heard another set of footsteps. He wanted to believe that this person would help him, but he had already been passed by twice and dared not even hope that he would stop.

The man who was travelling down the road this time was a stranger, who came from Samaria. People from Samaria were not very popular, so it was very unlikely that he would want to help. But as he passed by, he noticed the man who was lying by the side of the road. He felt sorry for him and wanted to help. He got off his donkey and bent down next to the man to get a closer look at his injuries.

Gently, he tore a piece of cloth which was in his bag and made bandages to wrap around the wounds. He helped the man to his feet and then he carefully lifted him onto the donkey. He took him to the nearest hotel, where he stayed with the man overnight and took care of him.

The next morning he had to leave, but when he paid the bill, he gave the innkeeper extra money, saying, "Take care of this man, feed him, and make sure he has everything he needs. If it costs any more money to make him well, I will pay it the next time I come by."

Jesus, after finishing the story, asked the lawyer, "Which of these three men was a neighbour to the stranger on the street?"
The lawyer answered, "The one who stopped and helped him."

Jesus said, "That's right. Now go and do the same."

This story tells of the love Jesus had for people and how he cared for them in many different ways.

LOAVES AND FISHES

News of the teachings of Jesus had spread, so that now, wherever he and his disciples went, people arrived in great crowds. People often gathered round, wanting to hear Jesus speak, or see him heal the sick. Often, they did not even have time to eat.

One day Jesus and his disciples went on board a boat and sailed to another part of the lake, so that they could have a rest. They landed and went to a quiet place in the countryside, thinking that they would be on their own. The people had seen them leave, however, and had worked out where they would be.

They flocked out of the cities and came on foot to the place where Jesus was. When Jesus saw that a great many people had come, he had compassion and spoke to them, healing the sick people they had brought such a great distance. But, in the evening the disciples came to Jesus and said, "This is a lonely, barren place, and the day has gone. Send the people away, that they may walk to the villages and buy food."

Jesus was too kind to send them away hungry, when they had walked a great distance to hear him and had been in the hot sun all day. He said, "They need not go away hungry, give them food to eat." But the disciples said to Jesus. "There is no food, the only bits we could find are these, which a young boy brought with him. We have only five loaves and two fishes," Jesus said, "bring them to me."

Then he told the people to sit down on the grass; and he took the five loaves and the two fishes and, looking up to heaven, blessed them and broke them into pieces. The disciples carried the bread and fish to the people and they all ate and had plenty, although there were about five thousand people there. When the disciples took up the food that was left, it filled twelve baskets.

Jesus not only taught the people and healed their sick, but he fed them when they were hungry.

Jesus was a great teacher and people came from far away to listen to his stories and to learn from him. This story tells of a man who changed his way of life after talking with Jesus.

JESUS AND THE TAX COLLECTOR

This story comes from a time when the Romans ruled the land of Israel and they made all the Jews who lived there pay taxes to them. The Jews thought that this was very unfair and they hated the Romans. They also hated the Jewish men who had gone to work for the Romans as tax collectors.

In the town of Jericho, near Jerusalem, one man was especially hated. He was called Zacchaeus and he was in charge of all the tax collectors. The Jews knew that Zacchaeus and his team took more money from them than they should and that was how Zacchaeus had become a rich man. Zacchaeus was very proud of his fine house, which showed everyone how rich and important he was. Zacchaeus, however, because of his dishonesty, had no friends.

One morning, news spread around Jericho, that Jesus was coming to speak. Zacchaeus had heard all about Jesus and his healing, his teaching, and his wonderful stories and was determined to see him. As he made his way across the town, he heard the noise of a crowd and, as he got nearer, he could see that they were gathered around a man. "That must be Jesus," he thought. He then realised that he was much too short to be able to see over the heads of the crowd and certainly no one would let him near, as he was so unpopular.

Then Zacchaeus had an idea. There were wild fig trees growing by the road and Jesus would have to pass beneath them. "I know," he thought, "if I climb up, I will be able to see Jesus and the people will not be able to see me." He did this and was well hidden beneath the leafy branches. There he waited as the crowd approached.

Then he saw Jesus, in the middle of the crowd. Zacchaeus was well hidden. No one could see him, but he had a really good view. To his great surprise, instead of Jesus passing by, he stopped directly underneath Zacchaeus and looked up. "Come down here, Zacchaeus," said Jesus, "I am coming to visit you at your house."

Zacchaeus could hardly believe his ears. He could not believe that this great man of God really wanted to stay with him and was being friendly to him. This, of course, was what the people in the crowd were also thinking. They were wondering why Jesus was being so friendly to a tax collector, especially to Zacchaeus.

They became angry, "How can a man of God go to the house of a dishonest tax collector?" they demanded. Jesus took no notice of their angry words and followed the excited Zacchaeus to his house.

There they ate and drank and talked together. Zacchaeus listened to the words of Jesus, telling him how God's love was for everyone, even for those who had taken a wrong path. Zacchaeus then knew that God loved him, even though he had been greedy and dishonest, cheating his fellow Jews out of their money. Zacchaeus also realised that his great riches had not made him happy.

From that day on, Zacchaeus was a changed man. He gave half his money to the poor and paid back all the people he had cheated. This meant that he was no longer a rich man, for he had little money left, but he had the happiness which comes from doing the right thing.

This is another story about Jesus and his love and care for all people.

THE MAN WHO WAS BLIND

Bartimaeus was blind. He lived in Jericho, which was a very busy place. At that time, there was no work for someone who could not see, so Bartimaeus had been forced to become a beggar and he sat by the side of the road and asked for money.

One day Bartimaeus heard that Jesus was coming to Jericho. He had heard many stories of the great teachings of Jesus. He had also heard of the love Jesus had for others and that he had healed people.

Bartimaeus did not know when Jesus was arriving, or which part of the town he would go to. He kept listening and asking questions. Sometime later, he could hear many people moving about and asked a passer by what was happening. "Jesus, is here!" someone said. It was then that Bartimaeus decided to ask for Jesus' help.

He followed the footsteps and when they stopped, although he had no idea where Jesus was, or how close he was to him, he began to shout as loudly as he could.

"Jesus have mercy on me!" he shouted. The people told him to be quiet. But Bartimaeus had no intention of being quiet. He shouted even louder. "Jesus, have mercy on me!" People around could not hear what Jesus was saying so they told Bartimaeus again to be quiet. Bartimaeus shouted several more times, to the fury of the people in the crowd nearby.

Jesus stopped talking and told the people to help Bartimaeus through the crowd and to come to him. Bartimaeus was so excited. He managed to get near to Jesus, who spoke gently to him. "What is it you want me to do for you?" asked Jesus.

"Lord, let me receive my sight!" said Bartimaeus. Jesus said to him, "Because you believe that I can do this for you, you shall see."

Bartimaeus suddenly could see. The man who was born blind and had never been able to see before could see. The first thing he saw in his whole life was the face of the man who had helped him. Bartimaeus had been right to put his trust in Jesus.

Jesus told this story of a man whose love for his son never changed, even though the son behaved badly. Jesus wanted people to understand that God's love never changes, that everyone is loved equally.

THE SON WHO CAME HOME

This is a story which Jesus told, about a man who had two sons. They lived on a big farm, for the man had worked hard all his life and done well. The two young men were very different from each other. The elder son was happy to be a farmer like his father and did not seem to mind the hard work, while the younger son, had a more adventurous spirit. He thought that life on the farm was dreary and boring. He had heard about cities across the river Jordan, where exciting things happened, and he was keen to go and see for himself.

He knew that his older brother would inherit the farm when their father died, but also that he would be entitled to some of the wealth, so he decided to ask if he could have his share now.

He went to his father and said that he wanted to travel, start a business and make the family proud of him. To do that, he would need money, so he asked if he could have the share which would have come to him eventually

The father loved his sons very much and he wanted to be fair, though this request made him very unhappy, for he realised that he may never see his younger son again. He knew, though, that if he forced the young man to remain on the farm, continuing to do the hard work demanded, that he might grow to resent him and his elder brother. So, reluctantly, the man sold off some of the land, to raise the money for his son. As soon as he had the gold in his hands, the young man went on his way.

He first went to a city on the other side of the River Jordan. There he had a great time. He bought fine new clothes and went to the races, to the theatre and to the stadium to watch the athletes compete. He partied, he sang and he danced with the new friends he had made. He became very popular, since after all, he was a rich young Jew with lots of money to spend. This was the life he had dreamed of."

The young man was so busy having a good time that he forgot about the business he had promised to start. He thought there was no hurry for him to start earning a living, for he had plenty of money in the bank. The day came, however, when he found he had no money left. He had spent all the gold which would have been his inheritance. He could not pay for another party for his friends, or pay the rent for his splendid room. Soon, he would not even be able to buy food.

He was not too worried, however, for he had many friends. They would throw parties and clothe and feed him, just as he had been doing for them for many months. He gathered his belongings, slung the bag over his shoulder and went to the home of one of his new friends.

"This is a little embarrassing," he said, "but I seem to have run out of money. I thought that I might stay with you for a few days until I decide what to do."

"I'm sorry," the friend said, frowning, "but we do not have any spare bedrooms. You'll have to go somewhere else." The man shut the door inhis face. Embarrassed, he slowly walked down the street to the home of another new friend. This friend also refused to offer him a place to stay. He soon discovered that now that his money had gone, his new friends had gone too. He was all alone, a penniless young man in a strange land.

He started to look for work in the city, but could find none. He decided that he might have a better chance in the countryside, as at least he knew about farming. He walked for miles in the hot sunshine until he came to a small store. He did not have any money to buy a drink, so he had to go to the water trough from which the horses drank. He immersed his hot face in the water and took several deep drinks. This was not the happy, carefree life that he had planned.

He went to many farms, but no one had a job for a ragged beggar, until at last, a pig farmer took pity on him and gave him the job of looking after the pigs. Now, in the sacred laws of the Jews, pigs were considered to be unclean animals. No Jew would have anything to do with them, but the young man had no choice, he had to earn money to buy food.

As he sat in his filthy clothes, alone with the pigs, he had time to think of what a fool he had been. He thought about the good life he had turned his back on, of the love and care his family had given him. He compared that with the people he had been fooled into thinking were his friends, the ones who had only been interested in what he could buy for them. He remembered how, when he had worked on the farm, people had respected him, but now he had no food, no shelter, no decent clothes and no friends. It was then that he decided that he would go home. He knew that he had spent his share of the money, so could not expect to be taken back into the family, but at least he could show his father how sorry he was and ask him if he could work on the farm.

It was a long, tiring journey home, living on scraps and sleeping by the roadside. No one would have recognised the young man as the wealthy farmer's son, but as the thin, dirty, tattered beggar hobbled along the stony track near the farm, his father knew him straight away. He ran with arms outstretched to greet him, crying aloud with joy that his son had returned. The young man tried to say the words that he had rehearsed. He tried to say that he was not worthy to be his father's son, that he wanted work as a hired farm labourer, but the father was shouting to his servants to bring robes and gold rings, sandals for his feet, to get water for him to wash in and to prepare a celebration feast.

The feast they had was truly wonderful, but when the elder son came trudging home from a long tiring day in the fields, he heard the noise of the music and dancing and he was not pleased to see his younger brother. He was upset that his father was so pleased to see his lazy, good-for-nothing son. He shouted to his father about all the years that he had served him and toiled on the farm and yet he had never had a fuss made like this. He shouted that his younger brother had done nothing to earn this feast, that he had wasted all their money and was now being treated like a prince. It was just not fair.

The father did not point out that he could have had a feast anytime he wanted, or that he was working for himself as the farm would be his one day. Although the father was sad to see his older son's bitterness, he understood how he must be feeling, so he said gently, "My dear son, you are always with me and I am grateful that we share so much. All that I have is yours, but your brother is my son also and though he has behaved badly, I am happy that he is back and that my family is together again."

In this way Jesus helped people to understand that the love this father had for his sons was like the love of God, it never changes.

Jesus was not only a very good teacher, but was always helping people too. This story tells how he healed a young girl.

JESUS HELPS JAIRUS' DAUGHTER

Some of the disciples of Jesus were fishermen and Jesus often went out with them in their boat. One day, Jesus and his friends were coming back in the boat when they saw a crowd of people waiting on the shore. Jesus was, by now, famous for his teaching and his stories and people loved to listen to him. As they came close to the shore, Jesus stood up in the boat and began to talk to the people gathered there.

Suddenly, there was a noise at the back of the crowd, someone was trying to make his way through the crowd to get close to Jesus. It was a man called Jairus.

Jairus was the ruler of a synagogue (a place of worship). He lived, with his wife and twelve year old daughter, in a busy city called Capernaum. Jairus' daughter had recently become very ill and her parents were very concerned. They did everything they could to make her well. They called in many doctors, who tried to help, but she did not get better. They were afraid that their daughter would die.

Now Jairus had heard about Jesus and the great miracles he performed. He heard that Jesus had healed the sick, the deaf, the lame and the blind. Jairus believed that Jesus could heal his daughter too. So when Jairus heard that Jesus was in town, he ran out of his house to find him.

Jairus searched and searched until he saw a large crowd of people and, thinking that Jesus must be there among them, he ran even faster to get to Jesus. When he found him, he fell to his knees at the feet of Jesus, pleading, "My little daughter is very ill. Please come and lay your hands on her, so that she will get well and live."

Jesus saw that Jairus had great faith in him, so he went with Jairus to his house, with many people following behind them. As they were walking a servant approached Jairus, and told him the bad news. He said, "Your daughter has already died, there is no reason to bother Jesus anymore."

As soon as Jesus heard this he told Jairus, "Be not afraid, only believe." Jesus took Peter, James, and John with him to Jairus' house. There they found that people were wailing and crying. Jesus asked them why they were weeping because he said the girl was not dead, but only sleeping.

The people all laughed at Jesus because they knew she was dead. Jesus told them all to leave the house and when they had gone and the house was quiet, Jesus took the parents into the room, where he took the little girl's hand. She suddenly opened her eyes and smiled at Jesus. Very soon, she was sitting up feeling quite well.

Jairus and his family were overjoyed. Jairus was glad that he had trusted Jesus, and put his faith in God.

 # Hinduism

INTRODUCTION

- Hinduism began in India thousands of years ago and is still the main religion of India and Nepal.

- Hindus believe that every person's spirit is part of the great spirit of the universe they call Brahman.

- This great spirit is everywhere, is eternal with no beginning and no end, and no form which can be pictured.

- The many Gods and Goddesses worshipped by Hindus each represent one aspect of this great spirit. They are all reincarnations of the one God.

- Three of the most important Gods are Brahma the Creator, Vishnu the Protector and Shiva the Destroyer. These three Gods are known as the Trinity.

- The Trinity represents the three energies the one God is made of. In each of us are found the three energies. When these energies are balanced an individual is closest to God.

- Hinduism teaches non-violence, truthfulness, respect for parents and the elderly, simple living and helping the needy.

- Hindus believe that you should live a moral life so that you will be born again at a higher level. If you do not do this, you may come back at a low level as an animal or an insect, to begin again to slowly rise through the levels.

- Hindus have all kinds of rich and colourful ceremonies. Most Hindus keep a small shrine at home. There are many temples, small and large, where people stop to pray and leave a flower to their favourite God.

Hindu people believe in Brahman, which means 'holy power', a divine spirit, which is in all things. Brahman shows itself to Hindus in the Gods and Goddesses they worship. One part of the Trinity is Lord Vishnu, the preserver of life, and this story is about him.

The story is from a time long ago, when it was traditional for kings to have more than one wife

THE BOY WHO NEVER CHANGED HIS PATH

Long, long ago in the land of India, there was a King who had two wives who were very different from each other. The first one, Sunita was very kind and gentle and loved her husband very much. They had a son, who, being the first born, would be King after his father.

The second wife, Suruki, was more beautiful to look at than Sunita, but she was proud and selfish and had a very bad temper. The King gave her everything she wanted and she ruled all the people in the palace, for no one dared to make her angry. She tried to keep the King away from Sunita and his son, as she was jealous of the fact that it was Sunita's son, Dhruva who would be the next king and that the King was so fond of the boy. When Suruki had a son, she decided that he would be the next King, even though he was not the first-born.

One day, the two princes were with the King and Dhruva was sitting on his father's knee when Queen Suruki came in. She was furious. The King always seemed to favour Dhruva over her own son. She pulled the boy from the King's lap shouting that it would be her son who would be King, not him. She sent the boy, in tears, back to his mother. Sunita tried to comfort her son, but she knew that the King always let Suruki have her own way.

That night, at bedtime, Dhruva was still worrying about it. "It's unfair," he said. "I know that my father, as King, has power and that Queen Suruki has power over him. Is there no-one with even greater power, who could make sure that people are treated fairly?"

Sunita looked at her son before whispering softly, "There is one. It is Lord Vishnu, who looks after all of us. He is kind and just and fair."

Dhruva became eager to find him. "Where do I go to look for him?" he asked. "Lord Vishnu is everywhere," his mother answered, "but when there is something wrong, he will come to earth to sort it out. He may be in the forest," she said, to soothe him so he would go to sleep.

Dhruva did not go to sleep, though. He got up and went to look for Lord Vishnu. The forest was dark and the trees were home to all sorts of creatures, but Dhruva was determined to go on until he found Lord Vishnu. The first creature he met was a great brown bear. He asked the bear if he knew the whereabouts of Lord Vishnu. The bear was so surprised that the young boy was not afraid of him, that he just shook his head and wandered away.

Next he met a tiger, which was about to attack him, when he calmly asked the same question. The tiger was so amazed by the boy's bravery that he turned and walked away. Later on, he met a lion which was roaring ferociously. "I'm looking for Lord Vishnu," said the boy politely. The lion was so stunned when the boy stood his ground that he just looked at him and walked away. On and on trudged the boy. He would never give up. He was tired and hungry, but he just kept going.

One day, he came to a small shed. It was the home of a hermit, who really did not want to talk to anyone, but he took pity on Dhruva. He told him where to wash and gave him some food. Then the hermit wanted to go back to his solitary life, so he told the boy to sit cross legged and say, "I bow myself before Lord Vishnu," ninety million times and that Lord Vishnu would come. The hermit was sure that the boy would get fed up after a short while and leave him in peace. He did not know how determined Dhruva was. The boy sat there saying the words over and over, without sleeping or eating. He would not give up.

Lord Vishnu, who saw all things, was amazed at the boy. He took pity on him and came down to earth and carefully carried the boy in his arms up to the heavens. There he gave Dhruva a great honour. He gave him his own place and Dhruva became known as the Pole Star.

The Pole Star stands almost directly above the North Pole and people discovered that it never changed its position, as other stars did. For hundreds of years, sailors depended on the Pole Star to guide them, for Dhruva the star, like Dhruva the boy, never changed its path.

In Indian tradition, sons take care of their parents as they grow old. This is the story of Rama, who had to leave his family for fourteen years to honour the promises that his father made.

RAMA HELPS HIS FATHER KEEP A PROMISE

Long, long ago in India, there lived a King whose name was Dasaratha. He was loved by one and all because he cared about the happiness and prosperity of his people. Even though King Dasaratha had everything to make him happy he was sad at heart because, although he had three wives whom he loved, he had no children and was worried about who would become King after him.

One of the King's advisors told him of a magical ceremony which might help, so the King agreed to take part. On the final day of this ceremony, a figure appeared in the huge flame, holding a bowl of rice. The figure said, "Take this rice, divide it amongst your wives and you will have the sons you desire." Then the figure disappeared.

Dasaratha took the bowl to his first wife, Kaushalya, and gave her half of the rice. He divided what was left between his second wife, Kaikeyi and his third wife, Sumitra. When a little bit of rice was left in the bowl, he gave it to Sumitra saying, "Here, finish it up."

Later that year, Kaushalya had a baby son and called him Rama. Kaikeyi had a son next and named him Lakshman. His third wife, Sumitra, who had been given two helpings of the rice, had twins. The boys all became great friends. Rama was the eldest son, so was the one who was to be King after Dasaratha. Everyone respected Rama because not only was he strong and handsome, but he was kind and honest.

When Rama and Lakshman were nearly sixteen, a wise man came to the King and asked if the two boys could go with him to the forest to get rid of the demons which disturbed him when he was praying.

Rama and Lakshman went along with the wise man and between them they managed to chase away the demons so that the wise man could pray in peace. Rama and Lakshman were ready to return home straight afterwards, but the wise man asked them to accompany him on a journey.

They travelled to the place where the King's eldest daughter, Sita, was about to pick a husband from the many princes who had gathered in the main city. Almost every prince wanted to marry Sita as she was very good and very beautiful.

To help Sita choose, the King had decided that Sita would marry the prince who was able to bend a very heavy bow and put strings on it. This was to be done in front of the assembled crowd of people.

One after another all the princes tried but could not lift it, let alone bend it and put strings on it. It seemed to weigh as much as a mountain. Finally the King was about to give up when the wise man asked Rama to try.

Rama prayed and then lifted the bow with ease before putting the strings on it. Thus he proved that he was the strongest prince in the assembly. Sita happily placed a garland of flowers round his neck, to show that she was happy to marry him.

When King Dasaratha was told that his son Rama was to marry Sita, he was delighted and asked if Sita's three sisters could marry Rama's three brothers. This was agreed and all four couples were married at the same time. Dasaratha then decided to retire and make Rama the King of the country. But things did not go according to his plan.

An evil, jealous servant woman spoke to the third wife, the mother of the youngest princes and asked her why she was celebrating Rama being made King when it could have been one of her sons instead. The woman reminded the Sumitra that having once saved the life of the King, he had promised to grant her two wishes, and she still had those wishes. "Ask for them now," said the evil woman." "Ask for your son to be crowned King and for Rama to be banished to the forest for fourteen years," the woman persuaded her.

When Dasaratha came to take her to the coronation ceremony, she was lying on the floor, sobbing. When he asked her what was bothering her, she reminded him of the promise he had made. "Yes, my queen," said the King, "I remember that and I will not break my promise. Ask for whatever you desire!"

"Crown my son as king and banish Rama to the forest for fourteen years." King Dasaratha was stunned. Never had he broken a promise. What could he do now?

Dasaratha whispered to his attendant, "Go and bring Rama."

When Rama arrived, his father was far too unhappy to speak. It was the queen who spoke. "My son is to be King and you are to be banished for fourteen years." "Is this what my father desires?" asked Rama.

"Your father is keeping his two promises to me," the queen answered.

"Then I have no choice, I must honour my father's word. If promises are made, they must be kept. Let your son rule. I will leave the country immediately."

When Bharat, the prince who was now to become King, heard about this, he was very angry with his mother for being persuaded by the evil servant. He went after Rama and pleaded with him to return and rule the kingdom. Rama very humbly refused, as he did not want his father's promises to be broken.

Hindus consider Rama to be an ideal son, who willingly undertook hardship in order to keep a promise and so save his father's honour.

This is the famous Hindu story of Prince Rama and his beautiful wife Sita, who are helped by ten thousand monkeys to overcome evil.

RAMA, SITA AND THE TEN THOUSAND MONKEYS

This story is about a King who, to keep his promise, had to send his first born son, Rama, the one who should have been King after him, into exile in the forest. This was because the evil queen, his third wife, had plotted to make her own son the next King. Before Rama left, Sita, Rama's wife said that she would go into exile with him. Sita was so good, gentle and kind that she was loved by everyone and Rama knew that the forest was not a safe place for his wife to be. He told her that it would be full of snakes and tigers, that they would have to live on wild fruits and sleep in the leaves, but she was so insistent that he took her with him. Rama's brother Lakshman went too, so that he could offer protection.

They walked and walked far into the forest, through the thick tangles of vines, until they came to the land of the monkeys. There they made a home from bamboo leaves and settled to a simple life, wearing rough clothes and eating whatever they could find.

Now the forest was full, not only of snakes and animals, but also of demons. One of these, a female demon, fell in love with Rama and wanted him for herself. When she realised that Rama would never leave his wife, she flew into a rage and went to her brother, the evil Revana, demon ruler of an island kingdom, shrieking that he must go and kill both Rama and Lakshman and then take the beautiful Sita away. Revana agreed to seek revenge for his sister and devised a wicked plan.

He turned one of his demons into a beautiful deer and sent it to graze near the river where Sita often walked. When she saw the deer, it looked so gentle that she longed to have it for a pet. She returned to their cottage and said, "I am lonely, Rama, and that deer would be good company." So Rama went to capture the deer while Lakshman stayed behind to protect Sita.

Some time later, Sita heard a cry, which sounded like the voice of Rama shouting for help. Lakshman did not want to leave Sita alone, but felt he must go to Rama's aid. He grabbed his bow and arrow, but before he left, he drew a circle of magic around the cottage and said, "Sita, you are safe inside this circle. You must not cross it, or harm may come to you." Sita agreed, telling him to hurry and go to the aid of her husband.

Sita sat inside the circle by the door of the cottage, waiting for her husband and Lakshman to return. It was not long before the evil Revana, dressed as a holy man in a ragged robe, came near and asked for some food.

"I'm too frail and tired to walk another step," he said. "Please bring it to me." Kind Sita collected some food and took it to the old man. No sooner had she crossed the circle, than he leapt up, throwing off his disguise. She screamed and ran away, but he caught her and carried her off in a golden chariot to his faraway kingdom.

When Rama and Lakshman returned and realised that they had been tricked, they knew that they would need help if they were to find Sita. They were in the land of the monkeys and had always got on well with them, so they went to the Monkey God, to ask for help. He knew of the goodness of Rama and Sita, so he sent them Hanuman, his special messenger, and ten thousand monkeys.

Hanuman flew down to find Sita and immediately informed Rama where she was. They marched to the sea, where the monkeys threw rocks and stones into the water to make a bridge so they could cross to the island kingdom. They then arrived at the city where Sita was kept prisoner and a terrible battle raged. Revana, seeing that he was not going to win, leapt into his golden chariot and tried to escape, but the God Indra had been watching and sent Rama a chariot drawn by swans. They flew like the wind, and soon caught up with Revana. Rama was able to shoot an arrow which killed the evil demon. Immediately, music filled the air and flowers fell from the skies. Good had, once again, overcome evil.

The years of exile were now over and Rama and Sita returned to their kingdom, where the new king, Rama's stepbrother, knowing that the kingdom rightfully belonged to Rama, gladly returned it to him.

Many lights were lit to welcome Rama and Sita back, to show that goodness and light had overcome darkness. The people of India never forgot that victory and lights are lit in every home at Diwali, the 'Festival of Lights', when Hindus remember the story of Rama and Sita and how good overcame evil.

This Hindu legend tells how a wise King finds an honest and true man to be his successor.

KING MAHENDRA AND THE SEEDS

Long ago, there lived a king named Mahendra, who was famous for his wisdom and righteousness. The people in his kingdom were happy because their great King ruled justly and cared for them.

The King, however, had one regret and this was that he had no children and so had no successor to his throne. As he grew older, this worried him more and more. His ministers were also becoming anxious and his people were becoming unsure about their future.

To solve this problem, King Mahendra decided to look for a person of good character. He announced throughout the kingdom that people were invited to the palace grounds and that from amongst the people present a successor to the throne would be chosen.

People flocked to the palace on the appointed day. King Mahendra addressed the people and told them that he would hand out seeds to each person present. The seeds were to be planted and whoever brought back the best grown and most colourful flowers would be chosen as the crown prince. "A person who can take care of plants and make them prosper can also make the kingdom prosper," the King told them.

The people took their seeds and went back to their homes.

Some weeks later, people started bringing flowerpots to the palace. There were some amazing results. There were many varieties of plants, of many colours all over the palace grounds, each pot bearing the name of the owner written in big bold letters. There were so many, that the ministers appointed a team of judges to help the King to select the winner on the appointed day.

One man, however, had not succeeded in growing a plant in his flowerpot. There was just the soil and not even a tiny shoot in his pot. When he brought his empty flowerpot to the palace grounds, people stared at him in disbelief. Some even laughed at him.

His pot sat amongst the rows of the most magnificent flowers that anyone had ever seen. The colours were breathtaking. The judges thought that it would be a difficult task to choose the winner.

On the day the seeds were to be judged, the whole population turned up at the palace grounds. They were all wondering who would be chosen, when the arrival of His Majesty, King Mahendra was announced. There were loud cheers as the King entered the royal pavilion.

The King asked the ministers to brief him about the efforts of the people and the ministers told him about the incredible variety of flowers which had been grown by the people. It was then announced that his majesty had decided to walk amongst the plants to savour the wafting scents of the flowers and to behold their colourful beauty.

Accompanied by his ministers and by the palace gardener, the King walked around looking at each flower pot, now and again making comments about the spectacular colours.

The time for the announcement of the successor to the throne was approaching and the King rose to address his people. He asked for the owner of the one failed entry to step forward and explain why his pot had only soil in it.

The man answered that he had tried his best, even adding more fertilizer and carefully watering the seeds, but that he was disappointed and sorry that he had been unable to grow anything. The King stood up and told the people present that he had chosen his successor and that it would be this man.

The ministers, the judges and the people were dumbfounded. They waited for King Mahendra to explain. "I was looking for a man with character and I have found him," he said. " I secretly had all the seeds roasted before I gave them out, so none of them would grow. The people who produced flowers must have bought other seeds."

The King went on, "I was looking for an honest man and I have found him. This man has shown strength of character, purity of heart, fearlessness, straightforwardness and truthfulness." The King went on to say that the qualities he was seeking were those outlined in the Bhaghvad Gita, the holy book of the Hindu faith.

Ganesh is considered by Hindus to be the bringer of success and the destroyer of evils. He is also worshipped as the God of education, knowledge, wisdom and wealth. The elephant head denotes wisdom, the tool in his upper right hand helps him move mankind forward and removes obstacles from the way and the rope in Ganesh's left hand is to capture all difficulties. The snake which runs round his waist represents energy in all forms and he is humble enough to ride the lowest of creatures, a mouse.

There are many different stories regarding the birth of Ganesh. Here is one of these stories.

GANESH THE ELEPHANT GOD

Long, long ago, the Goddess Parvati, asked her husband Shiva, if they could have a child. Shiva was not keen to have a baby, but Parvati desperately wanted a son and said that it would not be any trouble to Shiva, that she would care for the child herself.

This was in the time when all things were possible and one day while Parvati was going to take a bath, she rubbed the dust and oil from her body and out of it was created the figure of a young boy. She breathed on him with great love and he came to life. Parvati looked on him and thought he was so beautiful. She told him that he was her son.

To keep people away while she was bathing, Parvati asked the boy to guard the entrance. Soon after, Shiva came to see Parvati but the young boy did not know who Shiva was and did as he had been asked, blocking the way. Shiva was, of course, unaware that this boy was his son and was surprised to find a stranger at the entrance to his wife's bathroom. When the boy would not let him pass, Shiva became furious and there was a battle, during which, the boy's head was chopped off.

When Parvati saw what had happened, she was overcome with grief and screamed and wept. In order to soothe her, Shiva told Parvati that the first creature he saw the next day, would have its head removed and brought to her son. The next day it happened that the first creature Shiva saw was an elephant. It was travelling north, the direction associated with wisdom.

Shiva collected the head of the elephant and placed it on the child's shoulders and at once the boy came to life again, shining with a special beauty. Parvati was overjoyed and embraced her son, the elephant-headed boy, whom they named Ganesh, meaning 'Ruler.'

The other Gods came to see him, bringing gifts, for example, something to write with, bowls of sweets and beads. The Goddess Earth gave him a mouse to ride on and Brahma, the Creator, said that he should be called 'Ruler' and that anyone who wanted to make a journey, or start anything new should think of Ganesh. He also became known as the destroyer of vanity, selfishness and pride.

The Goddess Parvati was overjoyed to have her son back and she cared for him well. Ganesh became a great and wise God, who was well loved by the people.

The story of how Ganesh got his strange head reminds us that even the most difficult of obstacles in our lives can, if desired, be overcome.

This is a story which was first told by a wise man to a King. He wanted to make the King understand the glory and the greatness of the Hindu Mother Goddess - the Devi, who can overcome all evil.

DEVI AND THE BUFFALO DEMON

A long, long time ago two wicked brothers, Ramba and Karamba, decided to pray for sturdy sons. One prayed by a fire on the banks of the river, while the other prayed nearer the water. Indra, the King of Gods, was jealous, so took the form of a crocodile and killed Karamba when he was in the water. While Ramba was overcome with grief, a Sun-God appeared on his chariot drawn by seven white horses.

"If you are pleased with my prayers," cried Ramba, "give me a brave son who can conquer even the Gods and punish the God Indra."

Ramba's wife had a son, who was called Mahisha and was like a buffalo. The young Mahisha wanted to become the strongest demon ever and became known as the buffalo demon. He wanted to be even mightier than the Gods. He realised that first of all, he needed some help. So he climbed to the top of one of the very high mountains in the Himalayas and started to pray to Brahma, the God of creation. Brahma was so pleased with Mahisha's determination that he floated down before him on a white swan and asked, "What do you want?"

The delighted Mahisha replied, "Oh, great Creator! Since I am already the most powerful of all beings, my only fear is that I could be killed. Please make me live forever!"

"That cannot be," the Creator shook his four heads. "All creatures born must die at some time or another. Ask me for some other gift."

Mahisha thought he was clever enough to outwit the God. "Then let me not be killed by any bird, animal, man, demon or God." He did not mention women because he thought they were too weak to fight him. The Creator granted this request.

Armed with this great gift, there was no stopping Mahisha's cruelty or pride. Soon he had everywhere under his control, except for the heavens. He challenged Indra, the King of the Gods, and all his commanders, to open battle. Indra laughed in scorn.

"What! Am I to be frightened by this buffalo demon? Let us go and teach this creature a lesson." Indra rode into battle on his majestic white elephant, surrounded by other Gods who joyfully followed their leader. Vishnu, the Protector of the universe, flew in to help the Gods.

The war between the Gods and the demons was terrible. It seemed certain that the Gods would win until Mahisha used his powers of dark magic to create tens of thousands of other buffalo demons.

The Gods were no match for this terrible army and were defeated. Mahisha swept into the heavens and crowned himself on Indra's throne. The demons now had a free hand to terrorize the universe.

Some of the chief Gods, including Indra, escaped and went, with Brahma, to see what could be done. Shiva, the great destroyer said, "My dear Brahma! What can I do when it was you who armed the buffalo demon with such powers? The only way to get rid of him is to find a woman powerful enough to destroy him." With that advice, they went to find the great mother Devi, the most powerful Goddess of them all.

She was sitting meditating, high up in the golden mountains. "Oh Goddess, save us and protect us," they implored. They told her of the terrible cruelty and greed of Mahisha. "I have heard of this buffalo demon and his evil ways," she said. "Do not fear, I will find a way to get rid of him."

She devised a plan. Using her magical powers, she changed herself into a beautiful maiden, and she waited, sitting serenely in a mountain garden. Mahisha heard about the maiden who sat meditating amongst the sweet smelling flowers and when he saw her he wanted her for his wife.

He went to her, disguised as a man, and boasted about his wealth, his grandeur, his mightiness and his accomplishments. The maiden listened, smiled and said politely, "I have no wish to be your wife, and I am going nowhere with you." "But I have many treasure houses and servants and can give you anything you want. If you don't agree I will take you with me anyway," he said.

"That will never happen Mahisha," she said. In a flash, Mahisha threw off the disguise and charged at the Goddess, ready to attack, but the maiden had vanished, leaving in her place a blazing fire.

Mahisha was furious. He swelled as big as a mountain, pawing at the earth with his great hooves. The Gods came to see what was happening, dropping their weapons by the fire. The flames shifted, changed shape and out stepped Durga, the warrior side of the Goddess. She collected the weapons the Gods had brought, climbed onto her lion and in a voice like thunder said, " I am Durga, the warrior who destroys all evil. Beware, buffalo demon."

A mighty battle ensued, with Mahisha throwing the mountains about, stirring up the oceans with his tail and roaring. "Roar all you want," shouted Durga, "You will not roar long." She leapt onto his back and, as soon as her ferocious power touched him, he was finished.

The oceans calmed, the mountains became still and every creature in the universe danced with joy rejoicing that once again, evil had been defeated.

 # Islam

INTRODUCTION

- Islam is a way of life for millions of people.

- Followers of Islam are called Muslims, an Arabic word which means "I submit."

- Muslims believe in one God called 'Allah'. (This is the same God that Christians and Jews believe in.)

- Allah gave his message to a prophet called Muhammad, over 1,400 years ago.

- Muslims submit to the will of Allah, which they learn from their holy book, the Koran (sometimes written as Qur'an)

- Muslims try to follow the 'Five Pillars of Islam.' These are:
  1 To declare belief in one God, Allah.
  2 To pray five times each day.
  3 To give to those in need.
  4 To eat and drink nothing from sunrise to sunset during the month of Ramadan.
  5 To make a pilgrimage to Makkah (sometimes written Mecca) where Muhammad was born.

- Prayer is very important to Muslims.

  Muslims pray at dawn, midday, mid afternoon, sunset and at night

  They must face towards Makkah as they pray.

  In the mosque, a special arch shows which is the right direction to face.

  Before Muslims pray, they wash their hands, feet and face to prepare themselves to talk to Allah.

This story tells how Makkah became known throughout the world because of the birth of a special baby, who became the prophet Muhammad.

MUHAMMAD, THE MESSENGER OF ALLAH

About 1400 years ago, a child was born in a town called Makkah, in Arabia. The baby was named Muhammad, a name which became known all over the world.

Muhammad's parents died when he was very young so he went to live with his grandfather and later with his uncle and aunt. They were good people who treated him with kindness and taught him to be honest and true.

When he grew up, Muhammad became a camel herder and trader. He was very poor and had never been taught to read and write, but he was well known for his honesty and fair dealing.

A wealthy widow, a business woman, heard about Muhammad and his good reputation. She needed an honest, hardworking man to work for her so she employed him. She soon learned to trust and admire the young man and though she was considerably older than him, she asked him to marry her. They were married and lived happily together for many years.

In the valley of Makkah at that time, the people worshipped and made sacrifices to many different Gods. Muhammad was worried about this, for he believed that there was only one true God, Allah. He often went to a hill top cave to meditate and pray.

One day when Muhammad was praying to Allah in the cave, he heard someone speak. "Read," the voice said. Muhammad peered around into the darkness of the cave, trying to see where the voice was coming from. Again the voice said, "Read." Muhammad could see no one, but he answered, "I cannot read." Again, the voice came back, this time even louder, "Read."

"I cannot read," said Muhammad, by now feeling confused and frightened.

The voice spoke again telling Muhammad to repeat after it, "In the name of the Lord who created all things, the Lord is the most beneficent, who taught men what they did not know."

Muhammad said the words and then ran from the cave. When he got outside he looked up towards the sky and there he saw a shining angel. "Muhammad," said the angel, "I am Gabriel, and you have been chosen to be the messenger of Allah."

Muhammad could not believe his ears. He hurried home to his wife to tell her what had happened. She was delighted. "You should rejoice," she said, "Allah has chosen you to be his messenger."

From that day on, Muhammad went around reciting and preaching the messages, which were brought to him by the angel Gabriel. The commands to honour only one God, Allah, became known as the Qur'an, the holy book of Islam.

At first, only a few people listened to Muhammad's preaching, but gradually more and more people became his followers. Some, however, did not believe him and refused to change their ways, so Muhammad and his followers went to a different place, called Madinahh, where many people gathered to listen to the teachings of Allah's messenger.

After Muhammad had been preaching for over twenty years, he wanted to return to his birthplace, Makkah, and said he would go on a pilgrimage there. The non-believers said he could not return.

With the help of Allah, the city was conquered and Muhammad returned to Makkah. The people listened to the words of the prophet now and began to truly believe in Allah. They began to destroy the idols of the other Gods they had worshipped before and turned to one God, to Allah and the teachings of the prophet Muhammad.

This story tells how important prayer is to people who follow the Muslim faith.

THE NIGHT OF THE JOURNEY

One night while Muhammad was sleeping near the holy mosque in Makkah, (Mecca) the angel, Gabriel came and woke him up. "Come with me," he said, "I am going to take you on an amazing journey."

They went outside and there stood a wonderful animal whose name was Buraq. He was as white as snow, had the body of a horse and two huge wings on his back. Gabriel lifted the Prophet onto Buraq's back and together they flew through the sky to the city of Jerusalem. There, Muhammad met Ibrahim and Moses and the other prophets who had come before him and he led them all in prayer.

Then Gabriel brought Muhammad two goblets, one filled with milk and the other containing wine. Muhammad drank the milk, but did not touch the wine. "That is good," said Gabriel. "You must teach your people to do the same, for Muslims are forbidden to drink wine."

This special night, the night of the journey, was still to continue. Next, Gabriel took Muhammad on Buraq to one of the gates of heaven. This gate was called the 'Gate of the Keepers'. There they saw twelve thousand angels standing guard.

"Is this the true prophet?" one angel asked. "It is." replied Gabriel. So Muhammad and Gabriel were allowed through the gate and they went up through the seven heavens. In each of the heavens, Muhammad met the prophets who had gone before him. He met many, including Adam, Isa, Moses and Ibrahim. At each of the heavens, Gabriel was asked the same question. "Who is this?" Each time, Gabriel replied. "It is Muhammad, the prophet."

At last, they reached the seventh heaven and the Prophet entered Paradise, where he came before the 'Throne of God'. Allah commanded Muhammad to return to his people with the message that they should pray fifty times a day.

On Muhammad's way back down to Earth, he again met Moses, who asked him how many times the people must pray. "Fifty times a day," said the Prophet. "That's a lot," said Moses. "That is a heavy burden and some people are weak and lazy. Go back and ask if Allah will make the number less."

So Muhammad returned to the highest heaven and asked Allah if the number could be reduced. Five prayers were taken off, but when Muhammad met Moses, he again repeated that it was too many. Muhammad went back to Allah many times and soon, so many prayers had been taken off that only five were left.

"Whoever says his prayers faithfully five times each day shall have the same rewards as for fifty." said Allah.

Before the new day dawned, Muhammad left the heavens, got up on the back of Buraq again and flew through the skies back to Makkah. The story says that his bed was still warm, just as he had left it.

This is a story which the prophet Muhammad told to his friends and followers.
It tells of the importance of being kind to all living creatures.

THE DOG AT THE WELL

Once, a man left his home to go on a long journey. The day was hot and before he had walked very far, the sun beating down on him had given him a headache. He was tired, hot and thirsty and the grass in the fields he passed was scorched and brown. There was no sign of any water. "I am so hot and thirsty," he mumbled to himself, "surely I shall come to a well soon." A short while later, when he was beginning to think he could go no further without a drink, he saw a well by the side of the road. He rushed towards it thankfully, desperate to taste the cool water, but when he looked inside, the well was empty.

His disappointment made him even more anxious to find water as he hurried along the dusty road, hoping and praying that he would see another well. Before long, he came upon another, but this too was empty. The fields were dry, there was not a spot of moisture anywhere and the man was beginning to feel weak and ill. He plodded on. His throat was parched and he was beginning to feel faint. Just when he was going to give up, he saw another well. This time, he hardly dared to hope. He peered over the side and there, far below in the dark depths of the well, he saw the sparkle of water.

"Allah, be praised," said the man as he looked round for the rope and bucket to lower into the well. "On no!" He could not believe his misfortune. There was no rope or bucket. How could he get the water he so desperately needed? He could only think of one way to do it. If the water could not come up to him, then he would have to go down to the water. He climbed over the top and carefully made his way down, pushing against the sides of the well with his hands and feet. Eventually, he felt the cool clear water and he cupped his hands and drank and drank. "Praise Allah," he said and, when he felt refreshed, he started the long, difficult climb back to the top of the well.

Feeling much better now, he was just about to continue his journey when he heard a small sound. He looked around and there, whining sadly, was a dog, sniffing at the ground. The dog was panting with thirst and his eyes were glazed. He came up to the man and tried to lick the hem of the man's robe, where it had trailed in the water at the bottom of the well. The man looked at the dog, aware of its plight. "Why, you're as thirsty as I was." he said. "You'll die in this heat if you don't get a drink."

The man remembered his hard climb down the well and made a decision. "Wait here," he said to the dog. Into the well he went again, making the long climb down to where the cool water lay. There he braced himself against the walls while he took off his boots. Carefully, he filled each of the boots with water and then, since he needed his hands to push against the sides of the well, he clamped the boots in his teeth.

The climb up was very, very hard. The boots were heavy and holding them so tightly made his teeth hurt. His arms and legs were tired and several times, he almost dropped the boots, but he held on, climbing slowly until he reached the top. The dog was waiting and the man carefully opened the boots so that the dog could drink, his tail wagging happily. The man smiled and patted the dog. "Now neither of us will die of thirst," he said, before he pulled on his wet boots and went on his way.

Allah was pleased by the kind act of the man and all his sins were forgiven.

The prophet Muhammad ended the story by reminding his listeners that they too would be rewarded for being kind to all living creatures.

This is another Muslim parable, a story of everyday life which holds a deeper meaning. It tells how a man is made to appreciate what he has.

MAHMUD THE GRUMBLER

Long, long ago, in a country called Persia, there lived a man named Mahmud. He was a good Muslim and prayed to Allah each day at the appointed times. Mahmud was known as an angry man, who was always grumbling about something. The only time Mahmud seemed to be in a good mood was on Fridays. Each Friday at midday, when Muslims can go to the mosque to pray to Allah, Mahmud always went. He enjoyed this time and looked forward to it.

When Muslims go to the mosque, they take off their shoes and leave them outside. Some men have expensive shoes and some have plain shoes. Some men have good shoes and some have worn out shoes. The type or condition of the shoes is not important because it is by removing them before they go in that they show their reverence for the holy place of Allah.

Now, Mahmud was not wealthy and the shoes he had been wearing had fallen to bits. He had no money to buy new ones and was really upset because he would have to go to the mosque with no shoes on. He grumbled to everyone about his misfortune. He tried to borrow some shoes from his friends, but as they were going to the mosque too, no one could lend any to him. There was nothing else to do, he would just have to go to the mosque without shoes and he would have none to leave outside.

He went off to the mosque in his bare feet, grumbling and moaning all the way. "What a miserable life I have," he grumbled, "I am such a poor wretch. What a hard life I lead. I can't even afford a pair of shoes."

When he arrived at the mosque, he felt even worse when he looked at the pairs of shoes neatly lined up outside. People were admiring the beautiful shoes which the wealthy people were taking off. This made Mahmud even more miserable. "Why should they be rich when I can't even afford a pair of shoes. Why does Allah bless them and not me?" he moaned.

As he went into the mosque he was still grumbling about his misfortune. He knelt down and tried to join in with the prayers, but all he could think about was how badly Allah had treated him. He was not in the mood for praying.

He looked round at the other worshippers, wondering what sort of shoes each of them had left outside. He was feeling so sorry for himself that he had no time to think about Allah and why he was in the mosque.

Suddenly, he noticed a man kneeling in front of him and realised that he could not see the man's feet. He thought at first that they must be hidden under his robe, but then he realised that the man had no feet.

Mahmud suddenly thought about how he had grumbled about having no shoes, when this man had no feet to put shoes on. He immediately felt ashamed of his selfishness. His bitterness and envy were gone and as he reflected, he became more and more aware of all his blessings.

For the first time in his life, Mahmud thought of others instead of himself. He realised that although he was poor, he had much to be thankful for and that there were many people much worse off than he was.

Never again did Mahmud grumble. He was a changed man and news of his story spread. Ever since that time, there has been a well-known saying,

" I grumbled because I had no shoes,
until I met a man who had no feet."

This is the story of a young boy's bravery. It tells how his love for Allah and the Prophet Muhammad gave him the courage to trick some thieves.

THE BRAVE BOY

Centuries ago in a place called Madinah, there lived a boy called Salamah, who was famous for being very good at archery. He could shoot an arrow from his bow with such skill that he could hit a pebble on a distant stone, or a bunch of dates at the top of a very tall palm tree. Salamah was also well known for being a very good runner. He beat the other boys in every race and could often outrun grown men. Once he even ran faster than a horse.

Salamah was also known to be devoted to Islam and the Prophet Muhammad and would do anything to show his love and respect for Islam. He often ran errands for Muhammad and as he passed, people would say, "There goes Salamah. He can run as fast as a horse."

One day, Salamah was just outside Madinah, in the hot, dry hills, practising with his bow and arrow, when he heard a lot of noise. He ran to the top of one of the hills and looked down at the field where Muhammad's camels had been taken to graze. The commotion had been caused by several men on horseback, who were shouting at the camels and trying to chase them out of the fields.

"They're stealing Muhammad's camels," shouted Salamah, as he ran as fast as he could, looking for someone to help him. "Help, help," he shouted. "They're stealing the prophet's camels."

When he was sure that people had heard his cries, he started to run after the thieves. He ran like the wind until he was close enough to see them and the stolen camels. He was very afraid, since there were several of them and he was on his own. He jumped behind a boulder and keeping his eye on the thieves, quickly placed an arrow in his bow. He prayed that they would not realise that he was alone.

He shot arrow after arrow at the thieves, so rapidly, that they thought an army had followed them, until the leader caught sight of Salamah, hiding behind the rock.

"Why, it's only a young boy," he shouted to his men. "You cowards, are you afraid of a child?" The thieves were furious that they had been made to look fools and, forgetting about the camels, immediately turned their horses round and began riding after Salamah. He, realising that he had been seen, was running away as fast as he could. He ran faster than he had ever done before, but the thieves were getting closer and closer.

He ran up a hill and, seeing a clump of trees at the top of the hill, dived into it and hastily aimed an arrow. "If I can keep them away for a while, maybe help will come," he thought. "Allah be with me," he prayed.

The bandits circled round the boy looking for a way to reach him, but they could not get past the arrows which he shot from his bow. Salamah yelled at them, sounding much braver than he felt. "You'll never catch me," he taunted. The angry bandits ran back and forth, but each time they were stopped by the well aimed arrows. Salamah, though, was getting tired and he was running out of arrows.

Just as he began to wonder if the Muslims were ever going to arrive and save him, he spotted them in the distance. They dashed right into the group of thieves, swinging their swords. The thieves saw that they could not beat the Muslims, so they turned and ran away.

"Salamah has saved the prophet's camels! Allah be praised," the Muslims shouted as they went off to round up the camels and herd them home again.

That night, all the Muslims in Madinah gathered to praise the courageous boy who had tricked the bandits and saved Muhammad's camels.

"This story will be told for many years," they said. "Salamah will be remembered for his bravery, his cleverness and his love of Allah. His story will remind future generations that good can overcome evil."

This is another parable of the Muslim people, who follow the religion of Islam. It tells how a hardworking man helped his sons become proud of themselves.

THE TREASURE

Long ago, there lived a farmer named Abdullah, who had worked hard all his life and was a rich man with a fine farm and four very large fields. Everyone knew and respected Abdullah because he was honest and hardworking. He was a good man who was always ready to help anyone in need and although he was still wealthy, he had given much money to the poor.

Although everyone praised and liked the kind and generous farmer, they also felt sorry for him, for he had three very lazy sons. Hussein, the eldest, spent his time feasting, dancing and generally having a good time.

Ahmad liked horses and spent his time buying them and racing them. The youngest son, Hakim, enjoyed sword fighting with his friends.

The three brothers never helped their father with his work on the farm. They were much too busy enjoying themselves. In fact not one of them had ever done a day's work in his life, so it was not surprising that the local people felt sorry for the hard working farmer. The people often talked about how the three sons wasted their father's hard earned money instead of making their own livings.

The three brothers did not seem to feel any remorse for how hard their father worked. "Why should we work?" Hussein said. "Our father has plenty of money and when he dies, we'll have his treasure to live on,"said Ahmad. "And we can hire men to do the work on the farm for us," added Hakim. The three lazy sons carried on enjoying themselves, convinced that they would never need to do any work.

When the farmer was very old, he spoke to his sons. "I am leaving the farm to all three of you. You will find my treasure buried in the first field." Shortly after this, the old man died before they had chance to ask him exactly where they should look.

The brothers could hardly wait to get their hands on the money, so they rushed out and started to dig in the field next to the house. They were not used to hard work, so very soon their backs were aching and their hands were sore, but they went on digging, sure that soon they would unearth the treasure. They dug all the way across the field then all the way back.

Day after day they went on digging, and eventually, they had dug up the whole field but had found no fortune.

"We must be digging in the wrong field," said Hussein, "maybe he meant the next one." "He was very old," said Ahmad. "Maybe he forgot which field he had buried it in." They decided that they would dig in the second field. "Before we start," said Hakim, "why don't we sow some seed in the dug up field, then we can sell the crop and have even more money."

So the brothers planted wheat in the field they had already dug up.

They started work in the second field in the same way, still convinced that they would soon find the treasure and be able to return to their chosen pastimes. They were so disappointed when they dug up the whole field and had not found it. Once again, thinking of the money they could make, they planted wheat seeds.

Then they dug up the third field, but once again found nothing. By this time they were tired and disappointed, but now very sure that the treasure had to be in the last field. They dug this one up too, full of hope, but alas found no treasure. That field, they too planted with wheat. They were tired, angry and bitter, feeling that their father had cheated them. "He must have given his treasure away to someone else." they said angrily, "How could he treat his sons, like this?"

Before long, they had to get working again. The wheat had flourished in the fields they had dug so well and was now ready for harvesting. The three brothers worked hard and were rather proud of themselves as they took the crop to market. They made much more money than they expected and began to feel quite happy.

The fields were now empty and they again brooded on the lost treasure.

"I wonder if we didn't dig deep enough," said Hussein one day. "We might have missed it the first time. We might as well dig again." The others agreed, "After all, we're getting good at it!" they said. "We could sow more wheat," said Hakim, "look how much money we made last time."

So again the brothers, still hopeful, dug the fields, and once again were disappointed not to find their fortune, but again planted wheat. They had another fine crop and made a lot of money. For many years, they went on in the same way, still digging and hoping that one day, they would find the buried treasure. They now grew all kinds of crops and made a lot of money. The local people could not understand what had suddenly caused the three lazy men to turn into such hardworking, successful farmers.

One evening, the brothers were sitting together after a hard day's work. "Do you know? " said Hussein, " I think our father was very clever. He tricked us into thinking he had buried a fortune, knowing that it was the only way that we could be made to dig the fields. He knew that because we were so greedy, we would be sure to keep on digging and trying to find the treasure. In that way, he turned us into hardworking farmers."

"So the treasure was the money we made from the crops?" said Ahmad.

"It was more than that," said Hakim. "The real treasure was the way he showed us how to work together and to be proud of the results of our own hard work."

 # Judaism

INTRODUCTION

Today, Jewish people live in many countries, but their history began long, long ago in a region we now call the Middle East.

- One of the first Jews was called Abraham. He believed that there was one God, who had made the world and everything in it.

- Abraham's son, Isaac, followed in his footsteps and became a leader of the Jewish people, as did Isaac's son, Jacob.

- Many years later, God spoke to Moses, who became a teacher and a prophet. Moses received messages from God and these teachings were written down and became known as the Torah. Because of what God had told him, Moses went on to lead the Jewish people out of Egypt and into Israel.

- Jewish people meet to pray to their God in synagogues. On Friday evenings, they have a special family meal in their home and they celebrate the Jewish faith. Saturday is known as the Sabbath, a day of rest.

- Throughout the year, there are several special Jewish celebrations or holy times, when they fast, feast and pray.

This story tells how a young boy, on his first visit to a synagogue, finds his own way to pray.

THE BOY WHO DID NOT KNOW THE WORDS

There was once a poor shepherd boy who lived with his father up in the mountains. They spent all their time looking after their sheep so neither he nor his father had ever been to school and could not read or write.

The boy had seen very little of the world, so when he was thirteen, his father decided that it was time for him to go to the synagogue for the first time.

When the boy stepped into the synagogue, he thought it was the most beautiful place he could ever have imagined. The candles were lit, there were beautiful woodcarvings and there were scrolls covered in white satin and silver. The day of his visit happened to be a special day called 'The Day of Atonement', and the synagogue had been especially decorated.

The Rabbi, the religious leader, and all the people, were dressed in white. They stood up and sang a strange, sad song which haunted the boy. He very much wanted to join in but he did not know the words. He had a prayer book, but it was no help to him, as he did not know how to read it. He wished so much that he could have gone to school, that he could have learned to read and that he could join in and offer prayers and songs to God, like the other people who were there.

The service in the synagogue on this special day lasts all day and the boy sat spellbound. From dawn to dusk, he sat there, silent and still, watching and listening to all the wonderful sights and sounds around him. Then he heard them say that soon three stars would appear in the sky and that this would be a sign that the special day's service would end.

The boy was becoming more and more upset. He wanted so much to join in before the day was over. He wanted to do something to show God that he too was grateful, and wanted to praise him, but he could not think how he could do this. He thought and thought and then just before the stars came into the sky, he reached inside his old, worn, shepherd's jacket and pulled out his whistle. He put it to his mouth and blew on it with all his might.

The people stopped their beautiful singing. He blew again and some of the men turned to him angrily. He tried to blow a third time, but his father snatched the whistle from him. Several people were shaking their fists at the boy, shocked that their service had been disturbed in this way. They became very angry with the boy.

But the rabbi roared out,

"Stop! Do not be angry with this boy. All day long, we have sung and prayed, but our prayers have not reached heaven as clearly as this young boy's have. Our prayers are often not sincerely said. They do not always come from the heart. This boy's whistle was a true prayer. He prayed in the only way he knew. His prayer has reached God and we must all learn from him."

That evening the boy returned with his father to his sheep and the mountains. He was so happy that God had heard his prayers. He knew that it was not important that he did not know the right words. He had a sincere heart, so God had listened to him and that was all that mattered.

This story also teaches that adults are never too old to learn about religion.

This is the well known story of Joseph and his coat of many colours.

JOSEPH'S COAT

Jacob was very proud of his ten sons who were all strong young men. They worked on his farm, in the country which we now call Israel, digging the land to grow barley and looking after their flocks of sheep. Sheep were very important at that time, providing milk for drinking and making cheese and wool for making warm clothes.

Jacob was quite elderly when he had another son, Joseph. Jacob seemed to love him more than his other sons. He gave Joseph a special coat, which was long and beautiful and contained fabrics of many colours. It was the coat of a master, not the coat of a worker and was not like the clothes his brothers wore. It caused Joseph's brothers to be jealous and they began to hate him.

When harvest time came, Joseph's brothers worked hard in the fields, cutting down the stalks of barley and tying them into sheaves. One morning, Joseph said to his brothers, "I had a strange dream last night. In my dreamwe were all cutting down the stalks of barley and tying them into sheaves. My sheaf stood up tall and straight, but your sheaves bent over and bowed down to my sheaf."

In those days people believed that dreams were very important. They thought that God sometimes spoke to them in their dreams. Some dreams were hard to understand and only wise men could tell their meanings. Other dreams were so clear that anyone could understand what they meant. Joseph's dream was a simple one and his brothers saw its meaning at once.

"What is this?" they cried angrily. "Are we going to bow down to you, while you tell us what to do?" Joseph had several of these dreams which, foolishly, he told his brothers about. They were furious and now they hated Joseph even more.

One day, Jacob asked Joseph to go and see if his brothers were safe as they had been gone for several days, looking after the sheep.Joseph went to search for his brothers and they saw him coming when he was still a long way off, because he was wearing his coat of many colours."Here comes the dreamer!" they said to each other. Their hearts were full of hate and jealousy and now they saw the chance to get rid of Joseph. "Let's get him and throw his body into a pit," said one.

"Yes, and we'll tell father that a wild beast killed him," said another. "That will put an end to his dreams!" Reuben, the eldest of the brothers, was horrified when he heard this. "No!" he said. "You must not kill him. Look! Over there is a deep pit for storing water. It's empty now and we can put him in there." Reuben did not want Joseph to be killed and he had a secret plan to go back to the pit later and rescue Joseph.

The brothers agreed and as soon as Joseph came near they grabbed him, took off his coat and threw him into the pit. While the brothers rested, and Reuben had gone off to see to the sheep, some merchants came by with camels laden with precious things, like gold and spices. These were to be sold in Egypt. One brother saw the merchants and whispered to his brothers, "We could sell Joseph to the merchants as a slave, and get rid of him that way. After all, he is our brother and it is not right to just leave him in the pit."

The others agreed, so they lifted Joseph out and sold him to the merchants, who took him to the land of Egypt. When Reuben came back, and heard what they had done, he said, "How can we go back to our father without Joseph? This news will kill him." Then they had an idea. They still had Joseph's coat, so they took the coat home with them and showed it to their father, Jacob.

"Look, father," they said. "We found this on the way home. It looks like Joseph's coat. He must have been attacked by a wild animal and torn to pieces." Jacob was so heart-broken that none of his children could comfort him.

Joseph, of course, was in Egypt, working as a slave. After, some time, he became famous as a wise man, who could tell the meaning of dreams. Even Pharaoh, the king of Egypt, sent for Joseph to ask him to explain some dreams. One of the Pharaoh's dreams told Joseph that there would be seven years with plenty of food in the land of Egypt, followed by seven years when the corn would not grow and the people would be hungry.

Joseph advised Pharaoh to store up corn, so that there would be enough to feed the people during the years of famine. Pharaoh was so grateful that he made Joseph the ruler of the land and he made sure that when the years of famine came, plenty of corn had been saved.

One day, Joseph's brothers came to Egypt to buy corn. Their own crops had failed and they were hungry. It was then that Joseph's early dream came true, for there they bowed down to Joseph, asking for food, just as their sheaves had bowed down in Joseph's dream.

The brothers did not recognise this mighty ruler as the brother they had sold so many years before, but Joseph recognised them. Instead of revealing who he was, he played a trick on them, pretending to accuse Benjamin, the youngest of his brothers, of stealing a golden cup from him.

When he pretended that Benjamin would be thrown in jail, the brothers pleaded, saying that Benjamin was an honest man and that they would take the blame rather than let the young man suffer.

Joseph saw that his brothers were now honest men and had learned to do the right thing, so he told them who he was and they were joyously reunited. Jacob came from Israel and was delighted to find his long lost son.

Joseph was a good man who became a great leader and always tried to help others.

This story teaches the importance of belief in God, that things may seem black at times, but God is there, working in the background.

This is another story which has been passed down from generation to generation. It tells of a couple who were very honest and never went back on their word. They were also, however, very stubborn, which led to a great deal of trouble

THE STUBBORN MAN AND HIS STUBBORN WIFE

Shloeme and his wife Gittel went to bed one night and forgot to close the front door. In fact, they left it wide open. When they got into bed and felt the draught from the open door, Shloeme turned to Gittel and said, "You have left the door open, so you must go and close it."

Gittel had settled down under the bedclothes and was just getting warm. She did not want to get out of bed, so she said, "No, you left it open, so you must go and close it."

Shloeme had also settled down by this time, so he insisted, "I cannot do that, I said that you must go and do it and as you know, I never go back on my word."

Gittel was now warm and cosy in bed, so she also insisted, "I told you to close it and as you know, I never go back on my word either."

They continued to argue, neither of them prepared to give in, until eventually they agreed that the first person to speak would get up and close the front door. They lay in bed in complete silence, too annoyed to go to sleep, but by this time, the room was getting very cold and they were no longer quite as cosy under the bedclothes.

The wind howled through the little house and then, outside, it began to snow. The wind blew snowflakes into the house where they settled on the bedclothes. Icicles began to form on the shelves and on the old iron bedstead, but still neither of them would speak. They lay huddled under the blankets, shivering.

A short while later, some robbers could not believe their luck when they saw one of the houses in the village with its door wide open. They came into the house and took all the copper saucepans and the silver candlesticks. They quickly carried them outside and put them into the big sacks they had brought with them.

They came back in and took all the books and the clock which had been in Gittel's family for generations. Shloeme heard the noise and saw what was happening. He sat up in bed, but still he did not speak.

Then one of the robbers spoke, " I am hungry, let's have something to eat before we go on our way."

So they went to the cupboard and took and ate as much food as they could manage. Then they took the table, the chairs and the stove. They took the bookcases and they rolled up the carpets. Lastly, they took the curtains and the wood from the window frames. Still the stubborn man and his wife remained silent.

The thieves left. Their hands were so full of the stolen goods that they could not close the door. The next morning, Shloeme and Gittel got up and got dressed in silence. Gittel went out to find food while Shloeme sat on the floor in his empty house.

Meanwhile, a travelling barber who had called in the past to trim Shloeme's hair saw the door open, so came inside. "Do you need a haircut?" he asked. Since Shloeme said nothing, the barber began to cut his hair. When he had finished, he asked, "Well, how do you like it? Is it short enough?"

Shloeme did not answer, so the barber cut some more off. Then he asked him again, "Well, how do you like it? Is it short enough?"

Shloeme again did not answer, so the barber cut even more off. Then he asked again, "Well, how do you like it?"

Shloeme still did not answer, so the barber said, "You know, it might be better if we shaved it off completely."

Shloeme had not wanted his hair cut at all and certainly did not want his head shaved, but he was determined not to speak, so the barber shaved his head. The barber then said, "Now, you owe me twenty Kopeks."

Shloeme had no money, since the robbers had taken it all. He said nothing. The barber was furious, "What! You refuse to pay me?"

The barber was so annoyed that he looked around for something to throw at Shloeme, but there was nothing left in the house to throw, so he went to the fireplace and gathered up some black soot.

He rubbed it all over Shloeme's newly shaved head, before storming out of the house, leaving the door open. Some time later, when Gittel returned, she saw her husband sitting on the floor with a bald head, covered in soot and she screamed. "My poor Shloeme! What has happened to you?"

Shloeme stood up and jumped up and down with glee. "You spoke first!" he exclaimed. "Now go and close the door!"

"Why you silly, stubborn man," Gittel said, "do you not realise what our stupidity has cost us?" They stood side by side and looked around their bare house. Then they hugged each other and said they were sorry. "At least we still have each other," they said.

They had to work very hard to replace what they had lost, but from that day onward, they seldom argued, for if an argument began, one would remind the other of what their stubbornness had once cost them.

This story teaches us to take the good with the bad and have consideration for each other.

This is the story of how a mother put her faith in God, trusting him to care for her baby. The baby was saved and grew up to be a great leader of his people.

THE STORY OF MOSES

Many centuries ago, the Hebrew people from Israel, who were descendants of Jacob and Joseph, were living in Egypt. The Pharaoh, the King of Egypt forced them to work as slaves. He made them work in the fields, under the hot sun and make thousands of bricks from mud and straw. He made them build huge monuments and roads and cities. They slaved all day and yet they were often very badly treated.

Despite their misery, the Hebrew numbers increased until there were a great many of them. This made Pharaoh, the King of Egypt worried that one day they might turn against him, because he made them work as slaves. In order to prevent a time when there would be too many strong young Israelites, Pharaoh ordered that every new-born Israelite baby boy must be thrown into the River Nile. The soldiers marched into all the towns and villages and took way all the baby boys.

Now, there was a man and his wife who had three children, Aaron, Miriam, and a baby brother. When their baby brother was born, his mother turned to her daughter, Miriam, and told her that she was going to give this baby a chance to survive. The mother's plan was to put the baby in a basket, seal it with sticky tar to make it watertight and hide it in the bulrushes at the edge of the river. Miriam was not sure that this was a good idea, fearing that the baby would be swept out into the water, float away and be drowned. The mother said that they must try and that she would put her trust in God.

Hastily, Miriam helped her mother to weave a basket from reeds, and line it with soft blankets. They tucked the sleepy baby in and at the dead of night, they crept through the darkness to the river. They gently placed the basket in the bulrushes at the water's edge, where it was hidden from sight, before the mother bent, tearfully, to give her son one last kiss.

Miriam decided that she wanted to stay a while to watch over her baby brother, but the mother had to hurry back to the house so that no one would become suspicious. Dawn came and still the baby slept and Miriam dozed lightly, while continuing to watch over him.

All was quiet except for the sound of the waking birds when suddenly Miriam heard voices nearby. Peering from behind a bush, she was alarmed to see the Pharaoh's daughter with her maidservants. They had come down to the water to bathe. "Oh, no!" thought Miriam. She silently prayed that they would not see the basket, but of course, they did.

"Go and see what that is in the water, over there", Pharoah's daughter said to her maidservant. When the servant saw that it was a basket with a baby in it, she dragged the basket ashore and brought it to her mistress. The Pharaoh's daughter realised at once that it was a Hebrew baby. "Oh, he's adorable," she said and as she lifted the baby up, he began to cry with hunger. The princess tried to soothe him, rocking him in her arms. "There, there, little one," she said, "I shall take you home and care for you."

Just before the princess left, Miriam, who was still hiding in the bushes, came forward and took a chance. "Shall I go and bring a Hebrew woman to help you take care of the baby?" The princess agreed, and Miriam quickly ran to fetch her mother.

The mother was just getting ready to go out to work in the fields, when Miriam rushed in, gasping out the story of what had happened. "God has saved our baby," they whispered to each other as they hurried back to the river.

By this time, the baby was crying loudly as the princess handed him gently to the woman who, though she did not know this, was his mother. The princess said, "I will pay you to take this baby home and care for him until he no longer needs nursing. Then you must bring him back to me as I shall bring him up as my own son."

The mother was very happy and was grateful to God for the chance to be close to her child. The baby, whom the princess named Moses, as she had found him in the river, lived with his own family. As promised, he was later returned to the Pharaoh's daughter, who brought him up as her own.

No-one knew at that time, that Moses would grow up to be a brave, strong and good man who would one day lead his people out of slavery.

This story tells how a simple shepherd boy believes in himself and trusts that God will look after him. As a result, he bravely defeats the enemy.

DAVID AND GOLIATH

Long, long ago there lived in the country of Israel a boy named David. He was a shepherd boy, who spent most of his time in the fields with the lambs and the sheep. He was a thoughtful boy and wondered about the God who created this lovely world. Although David was only a boy, he was strong and brave and when he knew he was in the right, he feared nothing.

David's peaceful life as a shepherd did not last long. There was a great war between the people of Israel and the Philistines. All the strong men in David's town went to join the army of Israel. David could not go, as he had to tend the sheep, but his three older brothers went to the war. For a long time David's father heard nothing from his three older boys. After some time, he called David to him and said, "Take your brothers a bag of this corn and these ten loaves of bread. Find out how they are, and bring word to me."

The next morning David rose very early, and taking the bag of corn and the loaves of bread, he went to the camp where his brothers were. The camp of Israel was on the side of a high mountain. Across the valley from this mountain and on the side of another mountain was the camp of the Philistines. After David arrived at the camp and had found his brothers, he heard shouts of anger and fear coming from the soldiers.

David looked across the valley to the camp of the Philistines. Each day the Philistines sent their champion, Goliath, who was fully armed and gigantic in size, to shout across the valley. "Choose a man, and if he is able to fight with me, then we will be your servants. But if I kill him, then you shall serve us." David saw a huge soldier dressed in shining armour. The giant soldier carried a great spear and shield. "Who is that man?" asked David. "Do you not know? That is Goliath," said the soldiers. "Every day he comes out and dares any man on our side to meet him in battle."

"Do none of our soldiers dare to meet him?" asked David. "We have no man as strong as he in our whole army," said the soldiers. The giant from the opposite hillside shouted with a loud voice, and again dared the army of Israel to choose a man to meet him.

Now David was a brave boy and he became very angry at the sight of this great giant who was challenging the Israeli soldiers. "God is on the side of our people," he shouted. "I will fight with this man. Who does he think he is, that he should defy the army of God?"

The king of Israel heard of these brave words and sent for David to come before him. When he saw that David was only a boy, he said, "You are not able to go against this Philistine. You are only a boy, while he has fought in many battles." But David said to the king, "Once, when I was guarding my father's sheep, I killed a lion and a bear without help from any one but the Lord. He will help me to fight this man." So the king said, "Go, and the Lord be with you."

The king fitted David with heavy armour and gave the boy his own sword, but David said, "I am not used to this heavy armour, it will only get in my way." So he took it off. Then David went to a brook nearby and chose five smooth stones.

Armed with these five stones and his sling, he went bravely out to meet the giant. When the giant saw that David was only a boy, he was angry and cried out, "Do you dare fight with me? I will kill you, and feed you to the birds and the beasts." David looked at him without fear and said, "You come against me with a sword and with a spear and with a shield, but I come to you in the name of the Lord and He will help me. I am not afraid."

When they came near to each other, David fitted one of the five stones to his sling. He whirled the sling swiftly about his head and the stone flew straight to its mark, hitting the Philistine full in the forehead.

The huge giant of a man took one step and with a groan, fell to the ground. When the Philistine soldiers saw that their champion was dead, they were filled with fear. They left their camp and tried to run away, but the army of Israel followed them and won a great victory.

David was the hero of the people of Israel. He had shown that by trusting in God, having faith and believing in yourself, good can indeed triumph over evil.

This story tells how a brave queen saved the Jews from a wicked leader. Each year, at the festival of Purim, which is held in February or March, many Jews go to the synagogue to hear this story read from the scroll.

THE STORY OF ESTHER

Long ago, there was a time when the great kingdom of Persia, which stretched from India to Ethiopia, was ruled by a King who lived in luxury with his wife Esther. Esther was a beautiful woman, both in looks and in her nature and the King loved her very much.

The King's prime minister, a man called Haman, was a vain, unpleasant man, full of his own importance. He ordered everyone he met to bow down before him, and because most people feared him, they did. That is, all except a Jewish man called Mordecai, who happened to be Queen Esther's cousin. Haman met Mordecai in the street one day and Haman ordered Mordecai to bow. "I will not," Mordecai said calmly. "You will!" shouted Haman. "No, I will not," said Mordecai, quietly and calmly. "Then you will be sorry. You will suffer for your disobedience!" said Haman as he stomped away.

The wicked man, Haman, plotted to get revenge. He decided that in addition to punishing Mordecai, he would also punish all the Jews and he went to see the King. Haman told his master that the Jews in the kingdom were not obeying the laws which the King had made and that they should be punished. The King, without finding out what was really the cause of the problem, trusted his prime minister and told him to do whatever was necessary to sort out the problem.

Haman gave orders, which he said were from the King, that all the Jews in the kingdom, both young and old, should be killed. The people were shocked as the evil message was read out to them. As soon as Mordecai heard what was to become of, not only him, but all his fellow Jews, he sent a message to his cousin, the queen, to tell her what was to happen. He begged her to think of a way to save the lives of the Jews. The queen herself, as a Jew, was also in danger.

Esther put on her royal robes and went to see her husband. She requested that he attend a special banquet the following day, when she would have something very important to ask him. She also invited Haman. The wise queen was making sure that all the facts were heard.

The next day, at the specially prepared banquet, the King turned to the wife he loved so much and asked her about her request. "Whatever, you wish for, my dear Esther, will be granted." When Esther told the King what was happening, that all the Jews were to lose their lives and that she, as a Jew was also in danger, the King was shocked. "Whatever have these people done to deserve this punishment?" he demanded to know.

When Esther told the King that it was because her cousin Mordecai would not bow down before the vain Haman and that it had nothing to do with people not obeying the laws of the land, the King was furious. Haman, of course, could not deny the facts. The King had Haman removed and made Mordecai his second in command. There was great rejoicing in the kingdom when the news was received that the evil Haman had gone, and that the Jews were to be spared.

Queen Esther had shown bravery and wisdom in confronting Haman. She knew that getting people together to discuss the facts was the best way to reach a solution.

This story emphasises the importance of having faith, never giving up, and having tolerance for each other.

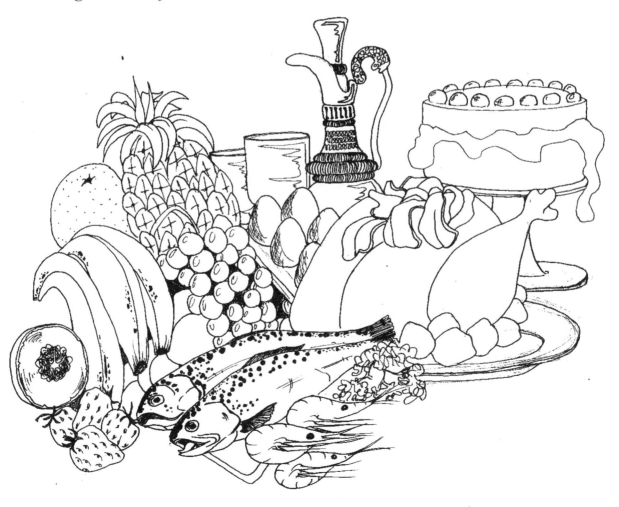

 # Sikhism

INTRODUCTION

The Sikh religion was started towards the end of the 15th century, in the Punjab, in India and now has a following of over 20 million people worldwide.

● It was started by Guru Nanak, the first of the ten gurus. He preached a message of love and understanding.

● The word 'Sikh' in the Punjabi language means "one who learns", Sikhs follow the teachings of the Gurus.

● Sikhs believe that the one God who created the world, is everlasting, all-powerful, sees and knows everything.

● Sikhism preaches a message of devotion and service, truthful living, equality of mankind and social justice.

● The true path to achieving salvation and merging with God does not require renouncing the world, but living the life of a householder, earning an honest living and avoiding worldly temptations and sins.

● All people of all religions are welcome to the Gurdwara, the place where Sikhs worship. A Gurdwara can be any place which contains a copy of the Sikhs' Holy book.

● A free community kitchen, which serves meals to all people of all faiths, can be found at every Gurdwara. Guru Nanak first started this, to outline the basic Sikh principles of service, humility and equality.

The word 'Sikh' means 'someone who learns'. This story tells how Guru Nanak, the first Sikh Guru, or teacher, helped a rich man learn that it is not having a great deal of money and many fine possessions which is important, but leading a good life and helping others, whoever they are.

THE RICH MAN AND THE NEEDLE OF HEAVEN

The first Sikh Guru, who was called Guru Nanak, spent a great deal of time travelling around India talking to ordinary people about how God wanted them to live.

On one of his many journeys, he went to a very large city called Lahore, where a rich banker called Duni Chand lived. Duni Chand was very proud of his wealth and lived in a large and beautiful palace in the city.

When Duni Chand heard that Guru Nanak was in the city, he rushed out to find him. He invited the Guru to a special feast which was to be held in the Guru's honour. The feast would be a very splendid affair, with the very finest foods and all the important people in the city present.

"Thank you, but no thank you," said the Guru. "I will not attend. I much prefer the simple things in life. Anyhow, " he added, " I would not want to cause you any trouble."

Duni Chand was very persistent and would not take no for an answer. Over and over he asked Guru Nanak the same question, until at last, reluctantly, the Guru accepted the invitation. Duni Chand was delighted. "It will be a splendid feast," he boasted, "You will have the very best time you have ever had and eat the finest food you have ever tasted."

The day of the feast arrived and it was indeed a splendid party. The food was delicious and plentiful and everyone agreed how wonderful it all was. When all the guests had finished eating, Duni Chand turned to the Guru.

"I am a very rich man," he said, "one of the richest in the whole city. If there is anything I can provide for you, anything you need or anything that I can do to help, Holy Sir, you have only to ask."

Guru Nanak sat for a few moments, thinking. He looked around him at the guests in their fine clothes, at the remains of the sumptuous feast, at the gold and silver goblets and the beautiful furniture.

He sat for a few moments longer before putting his hand in his pocket and taking out a small box. From this, he took a very small, fine sewing needle. "Yes, Duni Chand," said the Guru, "there is just one thing I would like you to do for me." Duni Chand's chest swelled with pride. "Whatever you ask," he trembled, feeling very important. Guru Nanak gave him the needle. "Please keep this safe for me and return it to me when we meet in the next world," he said quietly. "Of course, Holy Sir," said Duni Chand.

When the Guru and the other important guests had gone home, Duni Chand rushed to find his wife. He was desperate to tell her his wonderful news. "Guru Nanak must think very highly of me," he boasted, "to have given me such an important job. He has trusted me with the task of looking after this needle and returning it to him in heaven."

Instead of being proud of her husband, Duni Chand's wife burst out laughing. "Oh, you are going to do this for him, are you?" she giggled.

"And just how are you going to do this? Perhaps you had better ask him how you are supposed to do what he wants." She hurried away, still laughing.

Duni Chand was now very confused and hurried to find the Guru. "Oh, Holy Sir," he called to him, "please help me. How am I going to take your needle with me to heaven?" Guru Nanak looked at him and spoke kindly. "If this needle is so tiny and light and yet you cannot think of a way to take such a small thing with you when you leave this world, what will you do with all the great wealth and the wonderful things you have acquired? How are you going to take all of them with you?"

The rich banker realised the truth of the Guru's words and felt ashamed. His gold and his riches were worth nothing. Much more important, he realised, was to live a good life and enjoy what came from within.

From that day forth, Duni Chand really listened to the Guru's teachings on what is important. He gave his money to the poor, gave food to those who were hungry and did his very best to help those in need and when he left this world, he took a great deal with him in the form of many good deeds and good wishes.

There are many stories about Guru Nanak, and how he taught the importance of tolerance and acceptance of the views of others. In this story, he shows the holy men of Multan that there is room for everyone in the world.

THE BOWL OF MILK AND THE JASMINE FLOWER

Guru Nanak travelled to many cities in India, teaching people about God. Often on his travels, he was accompanied by a musician called Mordana, who had become his dear friend and faithful companion. One day, after a long and tiring journey, the Guru and Mordana approached the city of Multan. They had been travelling for many days and nights and were tired and hungry. Mordana was looking forward to a good meal and a long rest.

Now, at that time, Multan was an affluent city, famous for its many priests and holy men. People came from all the surrounding cities to consult these men, bringing them gifts of gold, jewels and money, in return for their blessings and advice. The priests and the holy men had become wealthy and greedy and did not want to share their good fortune with anyone else.

When they heard that Guru Nanak was near their city, they hurriedly called a meeting. "We don't want him here, he'll spoil everything," they said. "People will go to him instead of us. We must quickly think of a plan to show him that he is not welcome here."

They decided on a way to send a message to the Guru that there were enough priests and holy men already in the city of Multan and that there was no room for any more. They sent a messenger carrying a bowl of milk which was so full that there was not room in it for a singe drop more. This would take a clear message to the Guru, that there was no room for him in their city.

The messenger slowly and carefully carried the bowl to where Guru Nanak was. He held the bowl out slowly, making sure he didn't spill a single drop. "My masters have sent you this full bowl of milk," he said, "perhaps you have a message for them in return."

Mordana was hoping that the Guru would take the bowl and have a drink. Then he would be able to have some too. He was very thirsty. Guru Nanak did not take the bowl, however. Instead, he bent to pick a small, sweet smelling Jasmine flower from a nearby bush. The flower floated gently on the surface of the milk, spilling not a single drop.

"This is my message," said the Guru "just as there is room in this bowl for this small flower, there is always room in the world for more goodness and holiness."

When the messenger returned, still carrying the bowl of milk in which now floated a flower and he told them what the Guru had said, they were ashamed of their selfishness and their lack of hospitality. They apologised to Guru Nanak and Mordana and gave them a warm welcome to the city.

In this simple way, the Guru had shown that, in the world, there is room for everyone.

Serving others is very important to Sikhs. This story tells how Guru Amar Das, the third Sikh Guru, chose for his successor, a man who had the qualities needed to be a good leader and teacher. Sikhs believe these must include obedience, patience, devotion and service to others.

THE SEVEN PLATFORMS

Long ago, in the great city of Lahore, lived a man whose name was Jetha, which means, 'first born'. One day Jetha joined a group of people who were going to visit Guru Amar Das. Jetha listened to the Guru and was so impressed by his teachings that he stayed behind to serve him.

Jetha became famous for his humility and good service to others and did not change, even when he married the Guru's younger daughter. Jetha was always finding ways to serve others. Once, when the Guru wanted a well to be built, with steps leading down to it so that people could reach the water easily, it was Jetha who volunteered to help with the heavy work. Some people laughed at him, saying that it was not fitting for the son-in law of the Guru to work as a common labourer, but Jetha took no notice of them.

Now Guru Amar Das was a very old man and the time came for him to choose his successor, the one who would follow in his footsteps. The Guru's elder daughter was married to a pious Sikh named Rama, so the Guru had two sons in law from which to choose. A gathering of followers came to the Guru and said, " Both Rama and Jetha are equally related to you and both perform works with great devotion. Although Rama is older, you seem to favour Jetha. Would you please tell us why?" The Guru answered them. "I am looking for the one who serves with greater faith, devotion, humility and obedience. I am going to set a test for Jetha and Rama. Whoever fulfills my wishes the best will be the worthier of the two."

The Guru called the two men. He ordered each of them to make a platform for him to sit on. He would use one in the morning, and the other for the evening. He said that whoever did the better work would receive the greater honour. They began building, and after a time finished the platforms. Rama bowed to the Guru and showed him his platform; he thought he had done a very good job. The Guru looked at the platform and said, "It's crooked. Tear it down and build another." Rama said that he had tried very hard to make a beautiful platform to please the Guru. The Guru said he was sure this was so, but that he was not satisfied.

Rama built a second platform, yet this one also failed to please the Guru. Rama tore it down, but refused to build a third one. He mumbled, "The Guru has grown old, he is being unreasonable." The Guru replied, "Rama does not know how to obey, so how can he lead others as the Guru?"

The Guru then went over to Jetha's platform and treated him in the same manner, saying, "Your platform does not please me, tear it down and build another." At once, Jetha tore the platform down and built it again. When he had finished, the Guru said he was still dissatisfied and asked him to do it again. Over and over he ordered Jetha to rebuild the platform, so that he had to work all day and all night. Finally, after Jetha had rebuilt the platform for the seventh time, the Guru looked at him and said, "As this platform pleases me, so do you. As you have obeyed my order seven times, so shall seven generations of yours sit on the Guru's throne."

Turning to his Sikh followers, the Guru said, "I have tested both of my sons-in-law. You have seen why Jetha is my choice to be Guru after me. He has shown great patience and devotion."

Thereafter, Jetha was given the name Ram Das, which means 'God's servant'. He later became the fourth Sikh Guru.

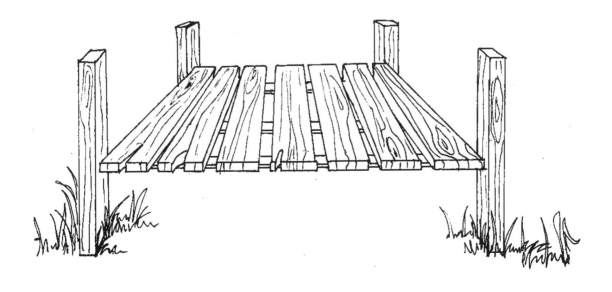

This story, about the sixth Sikh Guru, tells how he put the welfare of some Hindu princes before his own, showing the importance of treating all men as equals and of always thinking of others.

THE HINDU PRINCES AND THE GURU'S CLOAK

Guru Hargobind was the sixth Sikh Guru, who once saved the life of Emperor Jahangir, when a tiger attacked him on a hunting trip. After this the two men became good friends, though not everyone at the royal court was happy with this friendship. One of these court officials, named Chanda, plotted to get rid of the Guru.

One day, the Emperor became ill. He grew weaker and weaker and no one knew what to do to help him. The doctors were in despair, fearing for the Emperor's life. The Emperor called for Chanda to ask the court astrologers, to see if they knew what to do.

Chanda got the astrologers together, but before he let them see the Emperor, he spoke to them. "If you do exactly as I tell you, I will make you very, very rich." he said. Now, the astrologers were greedy and so they agreed. They went to the Emperor and said what Chanda had told them to say, that he would only become well if he asked a holy man to go to the fort some distance away to pray for his recovery. The astrologers, again following Chanda's instructions, suggested that Guru Hargobind should be the one to go.

The Emperor did not want to send his good friend, but was so worried about his health that he sent Guru Hargobind on the journey. Chanda's plot had worked and he was delighted to think that he had got rid of the Guru once and for all.

The Guru had thought that he would be alone in the fort, praying for the life of his friend, but when he got to the place, he found that it was being used as a prison and that there were as many as fifty two people imprisoned there. These men, though Hindu princes, were treated very badly, being made to dress in dirty rags, and given very little to eat.

The Guru was not treated in this way. He, though not free to leave, was well fed and was given a place to meditate and to pray. The Guru did what he could for the other prisoners, sharing his food with them and trying to get them proper clothes. He also tried to keep their spirits up.

Years passed and then a message came to say that the Emperor had finally recovered and that now he was well, realised there had been a plot to send his friend away from him. He ordered that Guru Hargobind was to be set free and return to the palace immediately.

However, the Guru did not accept this offer of release. He said that he would not leave the fort unless the other fifty-two prisoners were also set free.

The Emperor was amazed at this request. To release all those Hindu princes was unthinkable, but he wanted freedom for his friend. The Emperor sent a message to him saying that if the Guru would guarantee the good behaviour of the prisoners, then some of them could be released, but only as many as could hold onto the Guru's cloak when he left. The Emperor thought that he had been very clever. He knew that the gate of the fort was very narrow and thought that the Guru would only be able to take a few prisoners with him.

Guru Hargobind was also clever and thought of a solution. Straight away, he had a special cloak made with fifty-two long tassels. The princes each held a tassel, and thus, when the gate was opened, they all came out. The Guru's cloak had saved them all and they were all freed.

Once again, the Guru had shown the importance of treating all men as equals and of always thinking of others.

On reaching the palace, after his release, Guru Hargobind was greeted with a spectacular display of lights to mark his long-awaited return. People all over the city had lit lamps in their homes. This day coincided with the Hindu festival of Diwali. Diwali celebrations continue to this day, and Sikhs all over the world light candles and fireworks and give each other sweets.

This story tells how important it is to have faith in God. Sikhs believe that through faith, you will find out the truth. In this story, Makhan Shah's faith helped him to find the true Guru when false and greedy people tried to trick him.

THE FIVE HUNDRED GOLD COINS

When Guru Harkrishan, the eighth Guru, suddenly became ill in Delhi, he said that his successor would be found in 'Bakala,' a small village in north-west India.

Bakala was usually a quiet, sleepy place, but after the death of the Guru, large numbers of Sikhs flocked to the village looking for the new Guru. Suddenly Bakala was filled with people, all claiming to be the next Guru. Many of these were greedy people who accepted money and offerings when they had no right to do so. The Sikhs were in a quandary as to who was really the true Guru and this confusion lasted for almost a year.

Meanwhile a wealthy Sikh merchant called Makhan Shah was sailing along the coast of India. His ship was carrying a valuable cargo of fine silks and perfumes, which he would be able to sell for a great deal of money. Suddenly, a fierce storm blew up and the ship was tossed from side to side by huge waves. The rain lashed down and the wind howled. Never in all his years at sea had the merchant seen anything like it. His ship was being tossed about so much, that he feared that it would be smashed to pieces.

In despair, he closed his eyes and began to pray. "Dear God, if you will save my ship, I will give five hundred gold coins to the Guru, for him to help Sikhs everywhere. Please save my ship and my men."

His prayers were answered and he, his crew, the ship and the cargo arrived safely at their port. They had been saved. When he reached dry land, Makhan Shah immediately set out for Delhi, to honour the promise he had made. There he received the tragic news that Guru Harkrishan had passed away and that his successor was to be found in the village of Bakala.

So Makhan Shah set out for Bakala to pay his gold coins to the Guru. When he finally got there he was faced with the same difficulty as the rest of the Sikhs. No one knew who was the real Guru. There were twenty two people all claiming to be the real Guru and he could not tell which of them was telling the truth.

Makhan Shah had an idea. He decided that he would pay homage to all of the twenty two claimants and give each of them two gold coins. He thought that the false gurus would just take the money, but that only the real guru would know how much he had really promised in his prayers.

So Makhan Shah went from house to house, seeing each guru in turn. The first one sat on a beautiful chair which looked very much like a throne. "Thank you, my son," he said greedily. "Now, what else have you to give me? You are wearing some very fine clothes. What about those?"

Makhan Shah fled from the house, thinking that this man certainly could not be the real Guru, he was much too greedy. He went to all the other gurus and each one greedily took the two coins and many of them asked what other things he had to give. He had almost given up hope of finding the real guru, when a child pointed out to him that a holy man lived across the street. Makhan Shah asked about this man, known as Tegh Bahadur and was told that he was a quiet man, who minded his own business and though he was a holy man, he had never claimed to be the next Guru. Makhan Shah decided that he might as well visit him also.

Makhan Shah found the house and when he entered he found that Tegh Bahadur was meditating. Makhan Shah waited a little while and then placed two gold coins before him. At this Tegh Bahadur opened his eyes, looked at the coins and said to Makhan Shah, "What is this? When your ship was sinking and you were in danger, you pledged five hundred gold coins." Makhan Shah was overjoyed. "At last," he shouted, "I have found the true Guru."

He placed the five hundred gold coins in front of the Guru and ran outside to shout to the people that he had found the Guru. That night there was great rejoicing, for the ninth Guru, Guru Tegh Bahadur, had been found.

This story tells how the Guru helped some of his followers learn that all people are equal and should be treated with respect. He taught them about the importance of serving others, without any thought of reward.

THE HOLY CAKES

Once, long ago, an old woman, who was wise and good, but very poor, had a wish. She wished that the holy Guru Har Rai would eat bread which she herself had made. This would be a great honour and would make her very happy and proud.

Now, this woman made her living by spinning wool. One day she was able to do some extra work, which gave her extra money. This was her chance. She used the money to buy the flour and other ingredients for making cakes of bread. She made two cakes and took them to a place where she knew the Guru passed each day. She sat down next to the cakes, focused her mind on the Guru, and began praying. The Guru felt the strength of her prayer, mounted his horse and rode right to where she was waiting.

She had almost given up hope of his coming when he arrived. He said that he was very hungry from the ride, and wished to have something to eat. She offered him the cakes, which he ate on horseback, without washing his hands. He then said to her, "This is the most delicious food I have ever eaten." She was overjoyed and thanked the Guru for visiting her and accepting her hospitality. He shared his spiritual teachings with her and then blessed her.

The Sikhs who accompanied the Guru were astonished that he had taken food from a strange woman, eaten it on horseback and not washed his hands. They asked him why he had done so. He gave them no reply, but continued on through the forest.

The next day, they prepared sweet cakes with great cleanliness and carried them to the forest, where they met with the Guru. They thought that this would eliminate his need to eat unclean food from someone considered to be unworthy. After a while, the Sikhs offered the Guru the cakes they had made, but he refused them, saying, "The food you have made for me, with such great ceremony, is not pleasing to me, unlike the food I ate from that woman's hands."

The Sikhs replied, "O Guru, yesterday you ate two cakes on horseback from that old woman. There was no clean and sacred place to eat. The food was in every way impure. Today, with great care we have made the purest cakes, yet you reject them. Please tell us the reason." The Guru gave this explanation, "With great faith and devotion, that old woman made those cakes out of what she had earned by the sweat of her brow, by her toil and hard work. It was her love and desire to serve which made the food pure and that is why I ate it."

The Guru had shown them that something which is perfect, but has been gained easily is not as worthy as something, which although simple, has been achieved through true service and devotion.